Painting by Emma McKinley, Kinloch Rannoch Primary School

Introduction

BreadAtholl is, of course, a made-up hybrid word. It is meant to represent that area of Highland Perthshire from which the vast majority of the writing in this book originates. If Breadalbane is the east to west bit in the upper Tay valley, then Atholl is the north to south bit running between the hills from Blair Atholl to Dunkeld. *Brose* is the Scots word for a type of porridge but it also means a meal, or livelihood. This collection of writing is a good helping of honest endeavour and enterprise from BreadAtholl country. The book also serves as an example of whole-community involvement providing, and derived from, local creative inspiration.

Though the contributions come from two roughly distinctive areas, one thing unites them and that is heartfelt passion. From the youngest contributor, Hiba Saleem (6), writing about her hamster in Glen Lyon to the oldest, Allan Thomson (97 and a *real* hero) writing about the constant exposure to the possibility of death in the Second World War, the authors here invest themselves in their writing and we have another magnificent product as a result. The book was suggested by the success of a 2012 forerunner, *Life As We Know It,* which was experimental, and which set up the template for *Breadatholl Brose.* What the earlier book proved was that the community of Highland Perthshire has an embarrassment of enthusiastic writers all keen to tell their fascinating stories; old, young, men, women, locals, newcomers, migrants passing through and published and unpublished authors. This book carries that quality on. Many of the stories were inspired by the magnificent landscape on which they are based and they come both from poignant and instructive recollection and contemporary observation. We are lucky, and grateful, to have a sonnet from celebrated local author Kenneth Steven, entitled *End of the Year*, to get the book underway.

BreadAtholl Brose seeks to build on the foundation of *Life As We*

Know It and it has developed the approach and widened the net in terms of its community appeal and compass. The editorial team are grateful to local schools who threw themselves wholeheartedly into contributing and we thank the head teachers and teachers of Pitlochry, Glen Lyon, Dunkeld, Grandtully, and Kinloch Rannoch primary schools who put forward enough quality stories and artwork for selection to make a book all on their own. Future Highland Perthshire authors are ready to step into the shoes of their elders to ensure a continuing flow of quality creative writing from the area!

As noted one of the goals of the project was to involve the whole community and, whereas much of the writing came from individuals, a lot of the pieces were submitted through groups and have been part of a continuing learning process. Work was received from the *Jotters* writing group in Aberfeldy and those involved with *Crossing Borders*, an ESOL project (English for Speakers of Other Languages) in the area. Contributions were also made via the North Perthshire Community Mental Health Team, Fourways Daycare Service in Aberfeldy and NHS Healthy Communities Collaborative. Less formal groups such as the *Horizon* Lunch Club, *Knit and Natter* in Dunkeld, *Blethers in Ballinluig* and the Kinloch Rannoch Mums enthusiastically participated. Some of the photographs, including the evocative cover picture of Rotmell Loch, appear through participation with another Community Learning and Development project in the area, *The Big Picture*, which encouraged residents to submit their pictures of this beautiful part of the world. Local people selected their favourite picture for the front cover. Workshops in photography had taken place beforehand and so many area residents now have a better appreciation of digital photography with the most wonderful subjects on their doorstep.

As with *Life As We Know It,* many *BreadAtholl Brose* stories have been recorded by their authors for production as a radio series on local radio station *Heartland FM* as well as onto CD as 'talkies'. For this undertaking we have *Heartland FM,* and Bruce Patterson in particular, to thank sincerely for crucial assistance. The parallel availability of the stories through the medium of sound as well as print makes them accessible to a far wider community. Moreover they record the many diverse accents to be heard in the area and they uniquely constitute a form of living history which can, and will, be preserved for posterity. Thanks are also due to Jinty Smart for the dogged tenacity required for putting this book together, for her extensive list of local contacts and getting the book into its published state. Equal thanks are due to Pam McDonald, honorary Highland Perthshire person, for a different kind of dogged tenacity, namely the cajoling of individual authors, giving them the belief that their work genuinely does matter and deserves an audience. Pam would also like a special mention to Chris Meyer whose computing skills gave her great support in times of difficulty!

And finally we would like to thank the following organisations without whose support this project would not have been possible; the Hipshire Community Network, a group made up of voluntary and statutory organisations working to promote community learning in Highland Perthshire, Community Learning and Development, Perth and Kinross Council and finally the Heritage Lottery Fund whose generous support made this project a reality. Everyone involved wishes to record their gratitude to all these bodies, and we hope BreadAtholl Brose is a fitting testimonial.

Jim Finnie
January 2015

Pam and Jinty
would like to thank
Jim Finnie
for all his hard work, patience and
forbearance!

Contents

Drawing by Tiannaleigh Claughton
Kinloch Rannoch Primary School

End of the Year

November rain: the days like stinking dogs,

The colours of the hills washed out to sea,

The chimes of raindrops choiring through the trees,

Just singing day and night across the fog.

We made the house our cave, built up the coals

And watched their flames. We heard the clock

Click hour by hour, heard the pigeons flock

Their woods at dusk. We heard the owls,

Their ghostly murmur in the branches low.

At night we slept beneath the ringing eaves;

I dreamed of farms that floated south, their glows

Of lamps that lit their passage through the sheaves

Until they were no more. And then it froze –

One night the cold came hard enough to cleave

A stone. Next day the skies were snow.

Kenneth Steven

A Matter of Convenience

After an enjoyable, but hectic, week puffing and pedalling our way between Youth Hostels, Sadie and I had arrived at Corrour Halt (an unmanned platform in the midst of nothingness) where in anticipated solitude we awaited the arrival of the express that we hoped would stop and convey us homeward. Having had no idea of the timetable, we had come on spec and it was only after perusal of the data pinned to the wall that we realised we'd have a considerable time to wait.

With nothing to divert our attention save the brown, desolate moorland that seemed to stretch to infinity, we chatted, read our paperbacks or did nothing for ages, until Sadie was smitten with a call of nature. My suggestion that use be made of the surrounding terrain was treated with derision in case she should be spotted by some mythical person wielding a high powered binocular! (I should have told you that our Sadie is particularly sensitive to conditions you and I would take in our stride. More anon) However, needs or desperation must, and eventually she was cajoled into making use of the only alternative – an edifice marked 'Men Only' situated at the furthermost point of the platform. Lacking the possibility of intrusion into this male domain (that probably in days of yore had been provided for the convenience – no pun – of male dominated shooting parties) previous occupants had probably not bothered to lock the door. Consequently, either through disuse, old age or rust, the handle of the bolt disintegrated when Sadie shot it into its groove, resulting in her being trapped within the gloomy, windowless confines of the gents' loo!

As my well-intentioned commiserations were not appreciated, I eventually left the incarcerated Sadie to her screams and woes, to take up a stance at the furthermost end of the platform where I surmised the engine would come to a halt. Eventually it did, and after jumping aboard and quickly advising the rather bemused driver of our plight, he rushed to the aid of the victim and after yelling 'Stand back, Missus' banged the door open with his foot.

Meanwhile half the passengers within were leaning out making the most of the spectacle, even clapping at the emergence of the confined Sadie as she was led by her sympathetic rescuer to the privacy of an empty first-class compartment where I shared the luxury after seeing to the bikes.

No doubt the whole episode would give the trainload, and Sadie, something to laugh and talk about in the future, but what of the final fate of the damaged door!

Rhona Weir

Banshee

There was a time when my cry could freeze the waters from Bruar to Braan. A high hitting note that stopped hearts, birds fell to earth like stones. Sometimes the stars trembled. But no more.

Many, many winters ago, the bad freeze...

It began with a tickle in the throat. I had howled myself hoarse at Hallowtide predicting the death of the Earl's son. That wasn't unusual; I gave it my all for aristocracy. A full-throated threnody that made choirboys of the wolves. But the tickle turned to a wheeze, to a whisper – to nothing. I could no longer howl or scream or freeze men's blood in their veins.

Before I lost the use of my vocal chords completely I told my troubles to the owl. I made signs in the snow and squeaked a few words to articulate my predicament. She shut her great, yellow eyes as if sleeping. An owl will take her time replying, so I drifted across the moor until she had her reply.

Eventually the owl shook her snow-soft feathers and delivered her verdict blunt and without gloss, as only a wild animal can.

It could be throat cancer.

But am I not immortal, or at least dead? An imperceptible shrug of the owl's shoulders. The otherworld suffered all kinds of afflictions these days. An ill effect of living too closely beside mortals; the magic hinterland is disrupted.

The owl's judgement sent me into something of a crisis. For a century I became a stoat, ermine even in late spring. The next hundred years I flew through the mountain passes as a hoodie crow and then I became the hare that was never caught. But even

4

animals have their cares and eventually I transfigured back into a woman. A hag, to be precise.

Memories begin to fill the spaces instinct inhabited these long years.

I thought back to when I was wild and free. When my lands were the Tummel Valley, the peak of Ben Vrackie, burns and bridges, the desolate Moulin moorland. They were mine and I would speed down the golden slopes at the end of October shrieking blue murder, turning pebble, puddle and post to ice. I thought back to twilight evenings where I occasionally found myself washing a man's shirt, rubbing out the blood. Once upon a time it was soldiers' uniforms, the bullet blackened jerkin of a Jacobite. Sometimes it was difficult to work out whether he had died of his injuries or passed at the sight of me. A horrific little ghost of the moor, washing his bloody garments in the stream just like every legend he had ever learned. I like to think it was me. Now I only come into contact with the occasional hill walker. Sometimes I attempt to trip them up with a well-placed sheet of ice, but they are generally very sure footed.

I call to mind the winter of 1963, when I took more lives than I care to remember. Recently I gave records the worst winter in forty-five years. In 1437 I warned King James of Atholl's murderous plot. The court insisted on my legitimacy; I had the sight. (Though it is not difficult to comprehend the mind of a man who prowls his icy castle grounds at night, sharing his thoughts with the four winds).

Ah, those were the good old days, when they called me The Cailleach – ice-hag. Beira, Queen of Winter. The one-eyed witch, blue of skin, hair of snow. Or in more recent times, "the bloody weather". Before my throat cancer you could bet on icicles the length of your arm, the Tay hard as a diamond. Each year it is increasingly difficult to summon a good winter. The frost doesn't stick, and snow disappears as swiftly as it comes.

My greatest achievement in the last decade was the closure of several schools, resulting in children rejoicing across the county. At that point I acknowledged that my best years were behind me.

A banshee without her shriek cannot call back the dead or bring the living into death, she can only make her home in the hills as best she can, and survive, like the deer and robin.

Sometimes I wonder if I too will melt away with the snow. Capercaillie, grouse; their unsettled call rides over the strath, resonating nowhere, ceasing to echo. If I ever recover my howl then the river shall again stop in its tracks, the white cloak will yet cover the mountain. But folk will spring, melt water and thaw as they will away bad dreams, winter crones and the hard winters. A terrible shame, for there is melody in the January wind, if you listen, and beauty in bridal-white snow, if you see it.

Kate MacRitchie

Housewives' Choice

In 1954, when I was nine, my family left Inverness to move to a railway house beside the railway line at Black Tank, three and a half miles north of Struan where there was a station at the time. My father worked as a railway linesman. In our new house, we were lucky enough to have running water and a bathroom, although in those days we had no electricity. Tilley lamps supplied our light. My Mum kept hens and wee chickens by the side of the house. I often accompanied my Dad for a walk down to the nearby River Garry to search for wood for our fire. We collected armfuls and brought them back home to stack up and dry in the wood shed. As a bit of a luxury passing trains would sometimes drop off coal for us, and, on occasion, some milk, if my Mum needed it.

Other children who lived fairly locally would often come to my house and we'd play ball games in the garden. On nice summer days we used to go down to the river to play. We all had great fun, quite a different life style from that of Inverness. I attended school in Struan with my young sister. It was called Calvine School - an excellent wee school. My Mum made us a piece to carry in our school bags for lunch each day. The teacher allowed us to stand beside the radiator to get dry if we arrived at school soaked in the morning. If it was still pouring with rain at 4 o'clock, we were grateful when sometimes the schools' delivery driver, Mr. McNaughton, gave us a lift home. Sadly, our family home is derelict now. It's just a shell. I don't blame anybody for that because it's some distance from the main road and not very convenient.

I remember there was a wee train that sat in a siding all week at Blair Atholl: an engine and one wine-coloured carriage. Each Saturday it would come to life with the driver, the fireman and the guard in charge, leaving the station at Blair Atholl to travel up the line as far as Aviemore, stopping off at all of the houses along the track to pick up the families of railway employees on its route north. Sometimes I would accompany my Mum on her weekly trip on this train named locally "The Housewives' Choice". It was quite tricky to climb up into the carriage when our special train steamed to a halt for us – with no platform it was so high above the ground where we stood poised for its arrival. The guard threw down a set of wooden steps to assist our entry into the awaiting giant. We would get off at Kingussie where my Mum would stock up with the weekly messages at the Co-op. Later, laden with our supplies, we made our way back to Kingussie Station to catch the train on its homeward journey to Blair Atholl. After our busy shopping, we settled down in the train for the welcome trip south. I remember snuggling into those comfortable seats as the steam engine powered its way back down the track. No matter what the weather, even on snowy days, it still seemed to make this important journey for all those dependant local families. If there was a further need to top up on any household supplies, there was a grocery van which called once a week, where my Mum could buy vital things like the big batteries for our radio, our link to the outside world. No electricity – so no TV either! There was also a sweetie van that came to Struan once a week. My Mum would get us sweeties - a big treat!

Elizabeth Laverie

The Wedding Dress

It was hanging on the sale rail
Nineteen ninety nine
Reduced from nine hundred, size eight, it could be mine
I could start another diet
Gym three nights a week
Cut oot the Battenburg
Take ma vodka neat
I'm tempted, I'm tempted
To take this garment home

Hang it in my wardrobe, honeymoon in .... Eccelfechan
I'm tempted, I'm tempted
A bargain I can't resist
Keep it for my special day
Score it off ma list
The bodice, it was heart shaped
A flurry of luminous pearls
Satin buttons ran down the back
Petticoats and veils
The stitching was exquisite
The designer, yes had skill
The hem was scalloped with little lace bows
I will, I will, I WILL
I could wear my hair chignon style
That suits my swan like neck
My eyes were glazing over
As I slowly hit the deck
The assistant, she came running
Sat me on the chair
Wedding bells were ringing
HALLELUJAH confetti in the air
I could hear a voice in the distance
'Come forward please the groom'
Ted Baker, Calvin Klein, Paul Smith, Versace, Valentino
My heart went boom, boom, boom

As my eyes began to focus
Ma hand I did stretch out
The manager was such a gentleman, he whispered
'Yer teeth are somewhere about
yer glasses are tangled in yer hair and
yer hearing aid stuck in a teapot spout'
I managed to contain my composure
Whilst being directed to the door
Ma cheeks were as taut as a medicine ball
A left nothing on the floor
A felt a gentle tugging
A teenager's, aye request
Please release this garment
Sorry, sorry, SORRY I don't mean to distress
But I've four kids, a yucca plant and a Chihuahua
That constantly makes a mess
Oh and I'm getting married next week
At the Rewind musical fest
My conscious was instantly triggered
This request I could not deny
I've never even had a boyfriend
And I'll be eighty on the 4th of July
I opened my hand with reluctance and
Set this fantasy free
This wee lass was EUPHORIC
And squealed like a potbelly
'The taxi will pick you up at three'
The church was constructed of plastic.
Held up by gas and air
There were costumes of every description
And even the minister, she had pink hair
The ceremony was so emotional
The family all gave ME a hug
The best man was a bit shifty
Who ever heard of a DUG
I bopped, boogied and twisted

Danced to every conceivable beat
Until a young man tapped me on the shoulder
'Excuse me, your knickers are down at yer feet'
At eighty I roared with laughter
Invisible, I did not want to be
There could be a potential suitor, in the corner
Ready to proposition me
The church, it collapsed at midnight
Like Cinders, I had to run
Only to trip over an overindulgent reveller
And blocked out the midnight sun
In the morning whilst having my breakfast
Time to contemplate and relax
You know, I'd highly recommend shopping at TK-Maxx

Wilma McLauchlan

My Granny's Heilan' Hame

My granny's home was the East Lodge of Kindrogan Estate near Enochdu in Perthshire. Enochdu had a post office and a shop with a public telephone kiosk beside it. My grandmother lived as housekeeper to my Uncle John, who was a bachelor, after my grandfather died. My uncle was a gamekeeper and spent most of his time in tweed suits as they are the most waterproof of nature's materials.

I used to spend my school holidays with my Mum and brother at East Lodge. The water for the lodge came from a well sunk in a burn. The water tumbled in at the top and came out about half way down the boxed-in well so that items like twigs and leaves were not taken through the taps. The Lodge was lit by tilley lamps and my mother used to show my brother and I to bed with a candle. I'll never forget the hiss of the tilley lamps – it was a comforting sound - and they gave off an incandescent light. The house had no gas or electricity and the water was heated by a fireplace which was surrounded by five ovens, two on each side and a small one above the fire in which the kindlings were dried for the next day. My granny did all her baking and cooking here either resting pans on supports that swung over the fire or putting casserole dishes in the ovens to cook. We used to enjoy granny's cooking! She used to cook for the shooting lodge at Dalreoch on the Estate. She was an exceptionally good cook and Uncle John never complained about his mother's cooking! There was a zinc meat-safe outside the back door before the Lodge had electricity. It kept the meat cool.

I learned to play whist at an early age with my granny, uncle, mum and brother. Later on I went out to basket whist drives. Ladies each took a basket with four cups, saucers and side plates plus a cake stand with cakes and sandwiches. The ladies vied with each other to see who could come up with the best goodies. It was progressive whist which meant you went from one table to the next. After so many rotations you'd go back to your own table to eat the food your hostess had provided. Another activity I took part in with my uncle was at the Enochdu shooting range. This had a roaring stove in it – someone would stoke it up with logs earlier on. The range was lit by an electric light. The targets were lit up and you had so many shots at a target. There were several worthy characters at the rifle range. One of them was Neil Steele who was an out-and-out communist. I learned a lot of words I thought I didn't know the meaning of. Neil made their meaning perfectly clear as they were spat out with venom!

Fishing was also a very popular pastime. I heard an amusing story at the Enochdu social club. They were building a local bowling green but no one turned up on the opening night as everyone was away fishing! Fishing was the main hobby coursing through the veins of the people of The Glens. It was an easy sport to get into and relatively inexpensive once you were kitted out. Junior membership of the angling club was 1/6 and 7/6 a year for adults. My uncle was a keen fisherman and he taught me how to fish. The Brerachan burn ran next to East Lodge and I remember at the age of five going fishing with my uncle. We cut a sapling down and stripped the branches off it with his knife and added on some deep-sea line and a hook. Then I had to go and dig up worms in the midden. It was rich and I got a lot of worms. My uncle showed me how to put a worm on the hook and how to drop it in quietly. All of a sudden I felt a tug on my line. I immediately yanked my rod up and over and the fish flew over my head. My uncle laughed saying: "You don't have to do it so hard Fred!" We caught six fish in half an hour then they went off the take. My granny fried them in oatmeal and we ate them for tea. They were reasonably sized trout for eating and very tasty.

I remember one summer I was over with my brother and mother when I was eight. I had followed the Brerachan for a considerable way, the sun was shining and the water was sparkling in my eyes. I developed a terrible headache – maybe sunstroke – and when I got home I was in tears. My mother gave me some painkillers and I went to bed on the sitting room settee. I slept and when I woke up it had gone. I was glad – it was the worst pain I had experienced in my life. I got something to eat and drink and went back to sleep. From the settee I could see an armchair that my granny got from the Laird for 25 years' service. My uncle got a gold pocket watch for his 25-years' service.

I always thought I could sleep better in my granny's house; there weren't street lights shining through the window and I could get a better night's sleep than I could at home in my own bed. My visits to East Lodge, sadly, stopped when my uncle died. The accommodation had to be given up as it went with the job but my granny was rehoused in a cottage in Enochdu.

Fred Smith

Castaway

He grabbed me round my slender neck,

I could not shout or scream,

He carried me into his room,

Where he could not be seen,

He tore away my flimsy wrap,

And gazed upon my form –

I was so cold and still and damp

His feverish mouth he pressed to mine –

I let him have his way –

He drained me of my self,

I could not say nay,

He made me what I am Alas!

That's why you find me here...

A broken vessel - broken-glass –

That once held Bottled Beer.

Anon

The Night is Red

This night is red,
And I have too much dust in my lungs.
Anyway,
The next glass of "minor offence" will swallow it.
The unshaven face in the mirror says something
silently to me.
Like the Holy pictures,
There are shiny colours and a touch of peace,
Light,
Hope,
And candles.
In the south,
Simply here,
I've already forgotten how to dance a waltz;
The craving has gone.
At the moment I am touching gold rings,
Gold rings in her eyes,
Her eyes,
- Oh my God!
Now is too late
To let it be.
To paint tattoos on the God-like face
Somebody like her,
My country girl,
Who came to remind me of something.
Why.......?
Please, is somebody here...........?
Just spin me around,
And let me go to the naked floor.

Radim Hajek

Dear Diary

The golden sun shone through the window onto my hot dry face, as we drove on the bumpy road back to our house from our amazing trip on Mull. Resting my head against the leathery seat I felt really bored; my ipad had no battery. Gazing out of the car window I took in the countryside where I lived.

'STOP!' I called to mum. I had just seen a big enormous stag in someone's front garden. In addition to what I had just seen a feeling of joy ran through my veins so I asked mum enthusiastically to drive back. Silently I tiptoed out of the car and to my amazement there actually was a stag there. Courageously but cautiously I crept towards the beautiful animal keen to take a photo. As I stood there I felt really lucky to live in such a wonderful, magical place. The stag stood there just watching me with his big deep eyes and that's just my excellent life in Highland Perthshire.

Later that night I lay in my comfy bed I felt amazing and tired after my extraordinary day in Highland Perthshire. I thought to myself if I lived in a big city like Glasgow I wouldn't see a humungous stag standing there in someone's front garden, even although I live in a small village which means lots of travelling I love where I live.

Skye Murray-Trail
Grandtully Primary School

My Stone

It has been nearly 9 years ago when I first set my feet on the grounds of Perthshire in Killiecrankie. At the time I was just over 18 and alone in the world. I left everybody back in Hungary and decided to explore, venture and suffer on my own. I have to admit it was not easy at the beginning; I felt lonely and homesick quite often but I had to carry on otherwise I would have had to admit that I failed and I do not do that very easily. I arrived on a cold and foggy end of March day. I started to work the very next day in the Killiecrankie House Hotel as general assistant. I did split shifts but not mega hours. I felt so isolated and lonely. The weather at the beginning was not so great but it soon started to improve.

I think I can admit my first summer in the UK, the summer of 2006, was the best up till now and it allowed me to go out for a run most of the days by the River Garry. Sometimes this little time on my own was certainly the best part of my day as I was alone and could sit down on the same rock every time to watch the World go by as I cleared my head out of all the things annoying me. I could scream and cry without people seeing me and asking their silly questions. After this I could go back and face the adversity of another day in the Hotel. After a while I started to get used to the place and my new situation and this little trip to 'my' stone became a habit. You might be asking why to the same place as there were lots of places, but the view from there was brilliant and the rushing sound of the water was so calming. I just loved that place. It was so peaceful and quiet. I think I can admit that if I had not found this place so early I would have possibly shortened my stay in Killiecrankie as I could not have coped just on the hotel grounds.

Do you want to find it? Since my job made me move to North Wales last year I cannot make use of this anymore but somebody might benefit from it. Take the path from Killiecrankie. Go across the footbridge and keep following the Coronation Bridge path. Just stop where the 2 rivers merge into one and you can see Clunie Power Station. Is that not just perfect? I have even seen white water rafters there occasionally. I wish I could still do this on a daily basis as I so miss this part of my life (all I have now living in North Wales is to go on the Promenade along the sea with plenty of other people around watching whenever I go for a run, regardless of the time; it is certainly not the same).

But if we are talking about nice places I have to say my other favourite place in Perthshire is the Queen's View. I certainly did not visit this place every day but I have been there to see the different seasons. I loved the lovely autumn colours and the icy winter loch. And there is a funny personal fact about this place other than that I found it beautiful. In my 7 years in the Highlands I have visited the Queens View 7 times with people who played or play a major part of my life. On my last visit I have taken my little boy there to show him what a wonderful place it is where he was born just in case we can't go back there together again. The only reason why he did not visit 'my' stone is that he was still not able to walk as much and it is not accessible by pram. Hopefully one day he can visit it and I really hope that one day when he gets there in his life he will be able to find 'his' stone which will help him to keep going and achieve his goals just like me.

Agnes (Agi) Forgacs

The view from Agi's stone

06/25/2012

Agi with her son at the Queen's View

Perthshire Shenanigans

'Ee look, Ada, just look at that view. You don't see anything like that in Manchester.'

Ada sniffed and then glowered at Doris. 'How long have we stopped here for?'

'I think the driver said an hour. Look, they say you can see the mountains of Glencoe on a clear day. Isn't this just the most beautiful view you've ever seen?'

'There's no shops.'

Doris wished she'd brought somebody more appreciative on this trip; Ada was such a townie. 'Come on, Doris; let's get back to that coffee shop for a tea and some cake.'

'You go on; you can look round the gift shop as well. I'm going to stay here for a bit.'

'Whatever for?'

'Because I like it here. I want to savour the moment.'

Ada, clucking, waddled off down the hill, in search of cake.

****

Doris stood, gazing into the distance, marvelling at the brilliant blue of the sky reflected in Loch Tummel. She wondered if Queen Victoria really had stood in this very spot. The colours of the leaves were a glorious sight – October was a grand time to visit Perthshire.

'Hello, m'dear. Are you enjoying the view?'

Doris was startled. She'd been lost in thought.

'I am that.' She recognised the tall, dapper man that was on the same coach trip.

'I'm Ted. Pleased to make your acquaintance. Is your friend not with you?'

'Oh, she's just gone for a coffee. I'm Doris, by the way. Nice to meet you.'

Ted seemed to be quite knowledgeable about Perthshire.

Doris was impressed. 'How do you know all this? Have you been here before?'

'Yes, many times. This was a favourite spot of my wife's. She died last year; I wanted my first holiday alone to be to Perthshire.'

'Oh, I'm sorry to hear about your wife, although it's nice that you've come back here.'

They were interrupted by Ada, puffing back up the hill.

She greeted them with 'Oh, I see you've got yourself a gentleman friend while I've been away.'

Doris reddened. 'This is Ted. He's also enjoying the view.'

Ada looked Ted up and down.

'I can see that. Well, you've missed your cup of tea. The coach leaves in ten minutes.'

As they walked back down the path Ted asked if they would join him for dinner at the hotel that evening.

****

The coach rumbled along Strathtummel. Doris hissed 'There was no need to be so rude.'

'Rude? I wasn't rude. I speak as I find.'

'Yes, and what you find isn't always right, is it?'

'Humph. That Ted's got his eye on you, you mark my words.'

'Don't be ridiculous. He was just being friendly'.

****

'Look, Ada, look at all the deer running...'

Ada was asleep. It was a waste of time letting her have the window seat. Doris always was a pushover. Dammit, she would sit with Ted tonight at dinner. Ada could please herself.

Ada did please herself. She joined them.

'I have to say, the food's exceptionally good here.'

'That's not like you, Ada, to be so positive. '

Ted smiled. 'I agree - the food is superb. The service is excellent too.'

Doris toyed with her goat's cheese salad, annoyed that she'd let sarcasm get the better of her in front of Ted.

By the time they got to the coffee, Ada and Ted were chatting away like old friends. Doris made her excuses, saying she was tired and wanted an early night. Much later she heard Ada, fuelled by gin and tonics, lumber into their bedroom. 'Doris, are you asleep?' Doris pretended that she was.

****

The next afternoon they were sitting on a bench in Kenmore, looking at Loch Tay, marvelling at the views – except Ada, of course. However, when Ted suggested a walk along the beach, Ada was all smiles and simpers. Doris stayed put. When they returned, Ada said 'Ted's taking me to the theatre tonight. We wondered if you'd like to come.'

Doris hesitated. 'What's on?'

Ted beamed. 'One of my favourites. It's a Mike Leigh play – Abigail's Party'.

Well, she'd be blowed if she was going to tag along with that pair and yet, what was the alternative? Stay at the hotel with the oldies? 'Yes, all right, I'll come.'

****

Eleven o'clock saw Doris and Ada giggling, trying – and failing – to get out of the taxi in a dignified manner.

'D'you think we should've waited for Ted?'

Ada said 'No, not at all. He was more interested in that Ethel, with her low cut top and her peroxide hair. I'm surprised at him, I really am. And did you hear him say his wife had been dead for five years? That's not what he told you.'

Doris sighed. 'Well, I wasn't the only one taken in. Don't tell me you weren't just a bit smitten too. Shall we go on that trip tomorrow, Ada?'

'Where's it to?'

'Dunkeld. We can see the cathedral and the Hermitage...'

'Are there any shops?'

Yes, there's shops...coffee shops too, lots of them.'

'That sounds good. You know, Doris, I am enjoying this holiday.'

Lesley Christian

Jack Frost

It's a frosty morning. I can't believe I am alive after what happened last night. I have a clear memory of everything until it became very hot. I didn't understand the conversation: 'Two soups!' or 'Where is my steak pie?' How can you answer 'No more orders for ten minutes!' to this question? Words were flying in the air, people were shouting at each other. I could listen to them no longer.

I concentrated on the smell. It was nice, warm and spicy. The smells from the different pots and pans blended and swirled in the room. Four lights were on on the cooker, and also the oven was on. I was outside but could hear and smell everything. The heat started to tickle me when someone in a white shirt opened the hot water tap at the window. I felt sick, I fell into pieces and I melted into the environment.

I feel comfortable now. I have enough space to lie on. The road is getting busier as the sun keeps trying to show its face behind the clouds. It's noisy and loud. A family is coming towards me. It's a 'click' noise, and then the ground underneath me starts moving. I can hear the children: 'Look at this! This is beautiful! It looks like a bunch of sunflowers! How amazing it is in wintertime!'

I can feel the warmth underneath me again. The pain is sharply split into my body.

'What is this? Is this the 'home' feeling that my grandpa described to me?' He said: 'You will travel a lot before you'll find your home. You change yourself so many times before you become yourself. Sometimes it hurts but it means you are a loved one.'

I thought this is my last transformation when I heard the children talking about me.

It couldn't be my home, because I am forced to move away with a sharp tool and heat.

'Hurry up Daddy! I don't want to be late for school!'

'I'm trying but I left my gloves in the house. My fingers are freezing, and we can't drive with frostwork on the windscreen!'

Might those be the last words I hear today and it's time to move on? Melting down, falling apart, and travelling with the wind. This is my life, and the whole world is my real home.

Krisztina Talosi

Gladys' Story

I came to Aberfeldy 45 years ago in 1969 when my husband got transferred there for his work. He was a manager of one of the local shoe shops. My two children, aged 5 and 10 attended Breadalbane Academy, which was what it was called then. In the summer I helped out in the shop.

Since then I have become very interested in collecting old photographs of Aberfeldy and the surrounding area. Some of these are from old glass slides which I have managed to transfer to the computer. If anyone wants a picture of old Aberfeldy they know where to come!

Gladys Meek

Letter from Brazil

This is the first newsletter we wrote after arriving in Brazil in 1988 to work with the church in Social Work. Our son Callum was only 9 months old.

At last we're here in Brazil – in fact it's 2 months since we arrived and we now consider life quite "normal" here.

We arrived safely on the 22nd July after a tearful farewell to family & friends on the 21st. It was especially hard to leave with Iain's Dad having taken ill that week. This was followed by a long and exhausting journey to Brazil, which didn't go without mishap: Callum's pushchair got mislaid between Glasgow and London, he hardly slept at all between Paris and Sao Paulo and we were fog bound for an hour at Rio de Janeiro. Finally we came to Campinas to discover that some of our unaccompanied luggage had gone astray in Switzerland. If that sounds bad then at least it all worked out in the end.

When we got to Campinas we discovered we had a phone and could therefore dial direct to Britain, so even through the recent postal strikes we've been able to keep in touch and get constant news of Iain's Dad's recovery. The pushchair was found within a fortnight, mostly due to the kindness and hard work of a BA "hunter" in London. Our baggage, after travelling to Miami and Canada finally turned up and, thanks to the help of a Christian customs officer, there was no undue bother to get it all out of the airport. As for Callum, he may have cried all night, but he welcomed John Clarke (BMS Brazil Rep) who had come to meet us at the airport with a big grin and they have been firm friends ever since.

Our first sight of Brazil was lights breaking through the dark night as we approached the airport of Recife in North East Brazil after crossing the ocean. It was still another 1,700 miles to our final destination, but we were in Brazil. As we flew over day broke and we were amazed at the vastness of the country which we could see clearly from the plane once the fog had lifted after Rio. As we travelled down the coast we saw hundreds of towns and villages of various shapes & sizes - so many, but you don't see them on a world map – and the sea sending silver threads of rivers up into the rainforests. There were trees everywhere, but signs of erosion too: tracks of red dust scarring the green, and as we approached towns getting nearer Sao Paulo the red earth increased as the trees became fewer.

We stayed in Sao Paulo for a few days before we left for Campinas where we were to attend language school. There we found a much bigger town than we had expected. Campinas is a modern city of 1.5 million inhabitants – the biggest city in the state of Sao Paulo outside the city of Sao Paulo itself. It is a big centre for both commerce and learning. It has a large, modern shopping mall with all the big department stores represented as well as a large number of department stores in the centre of town and a hypermarket on the outskirts bigger than any we've seen in Britain. It is also a university town with a big emphasis on medicine: specialist surgeries line the streets on our road to language school. Campinas also has its own agricultural institute and experimental farm. However, right next to the hypermarket there are shanties and the recent election propaganda emphasises the need for programmes for the poor.

Our block of flats typifies Campinas in a way, with one of our neighbours being a medical student and another working in a city school which provides free meals for poor children. We live in a 2 bedroomed flat 20 minutes' walk away from the language school. There are about 24 flats in the block distributed over three sets of stairs. All the flats club together to pay for a caretaker and general maintenance and our next door neighbour is the president of the residents' association. She has been very good to us, explaining to us all the things we need to know with lots of patience and gesticulating and rejoicing with us when she sees our Portuguese improving. We have got to know some of the other neighbours too now and are beginning to feel we belong when we can stop and chat on our way up or down stairs. We're not altogether in an island of Portuguese, however. Another BMS couple, the Perrys , live up one of the other stairs and Callum has found a great playmate in their 2 year old daughter.

Our local church is practically across the road from our flat. We've been made very welcome there and have got to know quite a few people since we were invited to go on the church outing to celebrate Independence Day.

Language school varies from frustrating to enjoyable. Anne is moving quite fast through the book because of her background in languages, whereas Iain is moving at a slower pace but getting there nonetheless. The teachers are all very friendly and interested in our progress, both in the language and settling into Brazil.

Callum has reached great heights since he came to Brazil – so we've had to move everything breakable higher up. He started crawling within a couple of weeks and standing up holding on to furniture he now walks along the furniture quite skilfully and loves playing chases (especially when it's nappy changing time!) and pushing his ball or his toy car in front of him as he crawls along. As our first introduction to the language school we were able to proudly announce that we had discovered Callum's first tooth breaking through. Now he has three and for a while was into biting big toes. He still doesn't sleep too well at night though.

As I'm writing the fan is whirring in my ear creating a welcome breeze. Although for the first couple of weeks we were quite cold, for the rest of our time here so far (bar the odd storm where the temperature drops dramatically) it has been hot – and I mean 100 degrees Fahrenheit – and it's only just turned spring! However we have been told the weather is unusually warm for the time of year and more like summer. There has been unusually little rain creating poor crops and drought even in winter, so we're hoping and praying for a good rainy season in November/December. So as you approach winter think of us sweltering in the heat and longing for rain.

Postscript: After spending his first few years in Brazil, Callum has always felt a yearning to return, which he did in 2009 when he was 21. Although he had forgotten how to speak Portuguese, he soon picked it up again, had a go at Capoeira (a Brazilian martial art), worked with favela children & made lots of new Brazilian friends, keeping touch with them through Facebook. Those first few years in another country gave him a taste of international citizenship and he has since lived in China and learned Mandarin too.

Anne Walker

Anne, Iain and baby Calum with friends in Campinas

The language school where Anne taught

Off Road Biking

Cycling

To the fisherman's hut

By the River Tay

Off road track

Log jump,

Pull the handle bars up,

Gap jump

Get my speed,

Seesaw,

Balance,

Water jump,

Both wheels off the ground,

Cycling

Back home

Along the River Tay

Joe Baker
Royal School of Dunkeld

Nicusor's Story

My name is Dinulescu Nicusor Adrian and I come from South-east of Europe, from a country which is extremely beautiful and also extremely corrupted. I came to Pitlochry one year ago with a recruitment agency. I was pleasantly surprised by this little town like a wonderful story full of life and vegetation where birds and animals live a life as enjoyable as the people.

I visited beautiful places like the Dam Ladder which is also genial and helpful for the salmon. The mountains are full of trails to amazing places with lakes full of life. You can feed the ducks and the swan at the Cuilc lake, and at Faskally you can rent boats and fishing as well. It's wonderful! Thanks to God because I arrived here and I meet only kind people. Here I ask my girlfriend to be my wife so I start my growing life with her.

My only regret is that I'm away from my family; my mother went to Italy three years ago and we have not seen each other for one year and a half. I have no words to express my longing for it. In November we have the holidays and I hope that my mom can come home as well to heal the hurt from my soul. I am lucky because 4 years ago I met the girl who changed my life and we managed to make our own family.

That's my story. I wish everyone all the best. God be with you!

Nicursor Adrian Dinulescu

By Taybridge

Out from the crowd –
'God bless, boys!'
Bursts clear, loud;
No inhibition.

In the mist by grey Taybridge
Cold hands applaud these striding ranks,
Strange in desert fatigue
Stitched with battle patches
Won in blood; unflinching resolve.

Clean, youthful lines
Soften their hard, deadly intent
Pursued so far away - for me, for you -
In a land not of my world,
Beyond anything understood.

No swaggering dark plaids today.
But with Red Hackles flaring proud, defiant
- The Boys are home!

Skirling pipes stir the morning air,
Maintain the rhythm of the march.
No missing man formation.
No room for sentiment as those returned
Exercise a freedom we take for granted.

Dismissed from their ranks,
We reach out to shake hands
Before they muster for the photo-op
Around the cairn … amidst the ghosts.
While local politicians mingle, as they must,
Shaw looks down … and weeps.

David Grieve

Donald's Farming Days

I learned to drive when I was 17. I learned with Wilkie's Driving School at Scone and passed my test the second time around. I was happy.

Donald Laing started me off on the lorries. I met Donald through my Uncle Walter when I was about 21. That changed my life. It was something I wanted to do. I got to move lorries round the farm, but not on the road because I didn't have my HGV license at that time. I've always had a mechanical mind, right from about the age of 7. It was Donnie's idea that I should go for my HGV Test. Donnie gave me the lessons then I went for a week's course to the HGV driving school in North Muirton in Perth. It was good. That was when I started working on different farms like Mains of Errol, Daleally and Ardgaith. I lived in Scone at that time. I got a shot of my uncle's wee van to go to my work and I had a red Ford Escort of my own. I could put my hands to anything on the farms like repairing and maintaining farm vehicles and driving the lorries, tractors and combines.

Basically I enjoy getting stuck into any job. I like hard work, often working for long hours driving or on the farm, depending on the time of year. I've driven down to the Borders and up to the north of Skye at Portree and to Ireland. Now my life has taken a new turn: Donald Laing, his son Donald, Davie Laing and myself and my son Donald too are going to be involved in contracting work. We are a good team at working together. We've organised what we will do on a yearly basis.

Muriel, Sheila and Christine will work in the office. This will all start soon. I'm looking forward to it. We will concentrate on the Tayside area, perhaps up to the Highlands when required. We'll advertise on the internet and hope to build up good business. We already have good customers for a start.

Donald Robertson

Donald at the wheel of his P3 Ferguson tractor at Perth Show

Dunan

I'm back up the glen at my croft! I never thought of it as mine, until Uncle Alastair left it to me in his will. 'Dunan Croft, the cottage and 2.3 hectares of rough ground on which it stands.' That's how it was described in the letter on weighty paper, in a weighty envelope from the lawyers in Perth. When we got married all those years ago, I said to Duncan: 'It's my love of the landscape and my country, in that one corner of Scotland.' All those holiday breaks up there with Alastair and Aunt Jess formed me, as much as the longer times in Edinburgh.

Now, I'm sitting by the gable, in the westering sun, sheltered from the north wind. As I sit and look about, the familiar landscape is firmly etched by the angled sunlight; etched and tinged with a hint of gold. The light in this direction emphasises the shapes of the drumlins about me; I'm at the head of two Perthshire glens. Glenrighdall is down to the south, while the shorter, steeper Glen Fionne-leigh heads north-east. It is mid-August, and I'm surrounded by the heather in bloom; a light purple in the light, and darker in the shade. It swamps me with the sweet smell of honey, heather honey to be collected and stored by the bees in the hives down the road a bit. Both glens are smooth sided as I look down them, a result of the unimaginable sandpapering of millions of tons of ice, with embedded rock to scour the old ground. Later, as water takes its own good geological time, it is no longer ice, but fluid, cutting and shaping the base of the round valley carved by it, in its solid state.

If I look up on the hillsides, the gouged corries are there, great for sheltering deer, and keeping them some summer water in the tarn. Again they were formed by ice; the deer are merely taking advantage of a happy set of conditions. Foxes roam, teasing the gamekeepers, birds of prey fly over teasing even more. Hares sit stock still, until startled into explosive, jinking racing by predator or man. Grouse coorie down with grown broods, clattering into noisy flight at the approach of tweeded men in Land Rovers.

Adders hide, skylarks perform operatic arias in the theatre of the air, snipe fly high and drum down to impress their ladies. In the winter, snow will streak over the ground, and then consolidate into drifting sheets; deer will mosey off down the glen, some birds migrate, as do the humans in the nearby town, the rest work at cold weather survival. Hares will turn white, to hide against the snow; later they'll look foolish when the snow is melted. Spring will come slowly at first, then with a giddy rush; I'll be swamped by a sugary sweetness when the whins are in stark, yellow bloom.

As I sit, I realise that this landscape became a core part of me, leading to enjoyment of geography at school, geography and geology at University, and then a career teaching geography to sullen, uninformed pupils in the school at Inverleith. A break for family for ten years was a relief, then teaching again, but this time at Heriot's; the pupils seemed more inclined to identify with my enjoyment of the subject, and the importance it has for me as an individual.

Now, here I am, in what was to be heaven, but I am without Duncan. How aptly named is the stroke, the bolt from the unsuspicious blue. Sixty nine, fit one day, stricken and lain in bed the next. He only lay for two days; we talked to an unresponsive shell. Who would know how much went in? I certainly didn't. Teaching is behind me; retirement in front. I should welcome it, but don't really. If I'm honest, I'm afraid of long days on my own. Perhaps I will write, if I can see the point. Perhaps I won't last long; the doctor says I have a bit of heart failure. It doesn't sound good to me, but I am not dismayed. I can only hope the landscape will comfort, and maybe encourage me. Uncle Alastair grew potatoes; I think I'll make a start with that next spring. He always said a crop of tatties was good for cleaning the ground of weeds, and taste great as well. The sun has reached the hillside now and heat has gone. Indoors for a fire, a dram, and a book before bed.

Hamish McBride

The Capricious Computer

Rita has her own computer

And none of us could e'er dispute her

Competent determination

To master modern day's creation

In most respects she's done just that

And almost has the thing off pat

Except in one respect is thrown

'cos this one's mind is all its own

Most often gets the spelling right

But somehow try as Rita might

BIRNAM seems beyond its ken

And she is irritated when

Between the R and M lies D

And BIRDMAN is it speciality

Every night she stays up late

With efforts to eradicate

This letter of the alphabet

But she will do it, never fret

Yet not before it has its fun

And only then the battle won

Capricious one of many names

For something playing childish games

Ellen Thompson

Say Yes

One Friday evening in the winter of 1981 I was sitting in my home in Hamilton when the phone rang. This strange woman said, 'You were born on 22nd August 1947 and lived in Garrowhill in the outskirts of Glasgow. Also you were adopted' – all true!

'Who are you and what's this about' I replied. 'I'm your natural mother' ------ this grabbed my attention! I in turn asked a few questions and eventually said **yes** to meeting up with her; life was rather different after that. Saying **yes** again led me to a whole new world and a previously unknown family in Germany: a gorgeous half-sister and three brothers; nephews and nieces and so much more.

In March 2000 I was offered, and said **yes** to, early retirement – leading to amazing opportunities in politics and other areas. Life had its downs as well – a diagnosis of Parkinson's disease and two divorces eventually led me to reside in a chalet on the banks of the River Tilt, Blair Atholl in 2005. From this point things only improved: still visiting Germany, and in Blair befriending some truly wonderful people. One night in the Loft restaurant I literally bumped into a lovely lady who ran a local guest house – she asked me to join her for a meal – I said **yes**. We immediately hit it off and became firm friends. Shortly thereafter she moved to a flat in Edinburgh but we kept in touch. She phoned me one day in 2006 asking if I could provide accommodation for an American lady friend of hers for a few days as she was attending the Glen Fiddich piping championships at Blair Castle. I said **yes** – little knowing what I was letting myself in for. We had a lovely few days, she went home to America after visiting my friend in Edinburgh but we kept in touch by e-mail. She came back again the next year for the piping and I said **yes** to her invitation to visit her in California; in a lovely town called San Anselmo, just a little north of the Golden Gate bridge.

Well one thing led to another; this time we both said **yes**. We have now been married for almost 5 years and split our time equally between California and Scotland looking at each day being so special and feeling so lucky to have found each other. There have been lots of problems along the way but we regarded these as opportunities and challenges – it surely beats threats and worries.

We took our chances, and usually said **yes** to the opportunities that came our way rather than no. We've never regretted any of our decisions. Life is good, particularly if you are prepared to take a few risks and say **yes**.

Iain Hart

A Sense of Place

I'm looking out of my kitchen window, just as I have done many times a day for the past 18 years this October. Well the sink is placed here. I have seen all the seasons from here changing slowly, fast. Great weather, bad weather and not forgetting the extreme cold and snow of the winters of a couple of years ago. Watching nature in all her splendid glory and how these extremes seem to be corrected and dealt with by her.

I've just seen from the corner of my eye a large male hare with his to-be white winter coat growing in, bounding down the deer track that runs through the woodland that surrounds my back garden, or, as I like to think, my extended back garden. I feel I don't need to sit in front of the television and watch programmes like Spring Watch and Autumn Watch – I can just look out of my kitchen window and see the cast of hundreds.

Walking across the fields and along the tracks with my dog, I feel privileged that I am able to get so near to all this flora and fauna. A buzzard just in front of me, hopping from fence post to fence post, dappled sunlight through the ash tree leaves glinting on his eyes, is not bothered by my presence. The herd of deer that are frequent visitors to my garden are also not bothered by me being there.

When I'm outside there is most definitely noise, for want of a better word, for all the seasons. The deep faint hum that is summer to the sharp crack of winter.

I have witnessed all things from new beginnings, life, death and territorial disputes. I never realised robins could be so vicious. Now is the time for most trees to close down and begin their winter dormancy, long months of sleep. To slowly awaken in the Spring to start their life cycle again. It does not seem a long time to go.

As the sun that is already low in the sky starts setting, the sky is full of the noise of geese flying south. The bats have just started to come out to catch insects that are still about in the warm evenings that for the moment are still with us. I notice that there are three youngsters from this year with the adults. I would love to know where they spend their days in this woodland.

As the light begins to fade and the darkness of the night pulls in, you would think it would be silent – no chance. At this time of year the deer have started their rut and the deep booming of the bark will echo through the woodland as the light goes. The fox will add his bark, and if he has disturbed the roosting pheasants they will soon squawk the alarm that can be carried far in that silence. The Spring night would bring the owls hooting, getting louder and shriller as they sort out their territory, and as always, the continuous presence of the pheasants squawking. They are here all year.

Although the clocks will go back one hour in a few weeks' time, there will still be a dawn chorus and the life and death of all this will continue. I will help as much as I am able to, starting to fill the squirrel nut feeders, filling the seed feeders, the peanut feeders and even throwing out a lot of corn for the pheasants. The field mice will nip out of their deep winter burrows and help themselves to some of this extra food. I do hope that the couple of hedgehogs that I have seen are well fed and fat enough to find their winter place that will be warm and dry to sleep their long sleep of winter.

During the winter months I can stay indoors and keep warm and at the same time keep an eye on this vast cast. Knowing that in a very small way, in the larger scheme of things, I am helping Mother Nature with her work and getting to understand the sense of this place.

Lin Frearson

The view of Lin's world

Perils of Country Living

Several years ago I was living at the head of Loch Rannoch managing our holiday cottages. One week in a dark and dismal February, my daughter had been staying with me and, as I had no guests arriving until the Saturday, I decided to return with her down to Perth on the Thursday. I took my Golden Retriever with me, on the understanding that her husband would bring me back to Rannoch on the Friday evening after he finished work. I decided to stock up on shopping whilst down there and took the bus to the supermarket on the Friday afternoon. Surrounded by a sea of plastic bags there was no way I could return to their house on the bus so I called up a taxi. Obviously this driver had had a trying morning. He sullenly watched as I loaded up his boot and, apart from his terse 'where to?', the journey was carried out in silence.

At 5.00pm my daughter got a telephone call from her husband saying there was a problem at work and he would have to stay until quite late in the evening to sort it out. I rang home to see if my husband could help me out but there was no reply. Faced with the fact that I *had* to return home that evening there was nothing for it but to call a taxi. Reeling from the price quoted for the 70 mile journey, and agreeing that the fare would be paid in cash, I awaited its arrival. The taxi came up to the door just as the heavens opened in a tremendous cloudburst with the ominous roll of thunder in the distance. To my utter dismay it was the surly driver I had come back from Perth with earlier in the day. Again he sat and watched as we transferred my numerous bags into the boot and onto the back seat and as I and the dog squelched our way into the taxi, he growled 'I dinna want yon cur on my seat'.

As we made our way north the rain got steadily heavier and it sounded as though metal rods were bouncing off the roof. The flashes of lightning and the rolls of thunder showed that the storm was directly overhead and as the road was awash with water, I leant forward and suggested that if the driver wanted to stop and take shelter it would be alright with me. I was informed that he had driven in worse weather and wanted to get home as soon as possible. My poor dog, petrified with the noise surrounding him, started to whine but even through that and the storm I could distinctly hear the 'tuts' coming from the front seat. Surreptitiously I dragged the quivering beast from the floor and cradled him beside me hoping that the steam from my wet clothes and his pelt would hide us from the rear view mirror.

The journey seemed interminable but at long last we reached Kinloch Rannoch. Pushing the dog onto the floor as the driver's head swivelled to ask where my road was, I steeled myself for his outburst when I told him that in fact he had another 13 miles to go up the north side of the loch. If the atmosphere in the car had been noticeable on the way up, you could have cut it with a knife as we started off again. Finally the estate gates came into view and we proceeded down the drive. The rain had masked the pot holes and every one the taxi hit brought forth a volley of expletives from a now very angry driver. I saw that the house was in total darkness and the Jeep was missing. My heart sank. My house keys were on the same keyring as the Jeep's – I was locked out.

Just to make sure, I tried the door and then I had to tell my surly driver that I couldn't give him cash but he would have to take a cheque. I took the bags from the taxi and piled them on the ground and then with frozen fingers wrote out the cheque, which was snatched from my hand with the speed of a conjurer and the driver slammed the gear into reverse and sped off leaving me and the quivering dog in complete darkness.

Although the storm had abated it was still raining heavily and gingerly I felt my way around the front of the house praying that one of the windows would allow me access. The Gods were with me and the top half of one of the smaller windows had not been securely latched and by banging it hard I managed to get it open. This hopper window when open was approximately 2 foot by 18 inches. Knowing that there was no hope of my getting through it with my winter clothes on, I started to do a bizarre striptease. My dog, delighted to be out in the open and sensing a game, bounced around me shaking each garment as it hit the ground and pranced over and over the bags of shopping lying on the ground. Now almost stripped naked and frozen from the continuing rain I squeezed my head and shoulders through the gap. Not being a sylph, it took quite a while to pull and push my body inside. Each inch took another layer of skin off my spine from the window catch then finally, accompanied by the frenzied barking of my dog who didn't want to be left on his own outside, I slithered inside onto the floor. I could have quite happily lain there but by this time the bottom half of the window was in danger of being smashed by the dog. I went to another room where there was a larger window from which opened outward and calling the dog dragged him in. There was no back door to the house. With the front door locked I had to go back outside using the larger window and throw my now-smashed-to-pieces bags of shopping inside along with my sodden clothes.

A shower to unfreeze me was vital and as I stood under the welcoming hot water, I warmed the inside of me with the thoughts of what I was going to do to my husband when I got my hands on him. Finally, feeling human again, I made my way to the kitchen where on the table was a note telling me my husband had had to go down to his sister because she had locked herself out – the irony was not lost on me.

Next morning saw a repeat performance as the only way I had out of the house was via the window but this time I had to take out the cleaning apparatus to freshen up the cottage for the guest coming later on. Heaving out the heavy electric cleaner and my box of utensils, I made my way past the front door. The bulky machine walloped an earthenware pot and, as I turned, I watched it fall over onto its side shattering into pieces, spewing out the soil and flowers and disclosing, shining brightly in the morning sunshine, my front door key which had been nestling there underneath it

Jacqueline Smith

After the Rain

You would have loved
The walk I took today

Beneath Castle Menzies (haunted, they say)
In the hollow of the field, a wee flood-lochan
As blue as your eyes

Above and to the South, the ardent spring sun
Blithely kissed the snow above Kenmore
With light as fey and fleet as innocence

And, sighing a promise of warmth and life,
A brisk-heart breeze sifted through
The grey-tawn wintered wheat

In the shadows ahead of me
A black smudge warned and wavered; the dog;
As carefree and joy-bound as truth

The walk I took today
You would have loved

Bec Cameron

Onward and Upward

This is a story about when I changed my life and left my fiancé. We both had good jobs and lived comfortably, but ultimately I was very unhappy. In November 2010 I moved in with my sister and brother-in-law. To start off with I thought, I'll sell off all my stuff; boxes and boxes, jam packed full. The bedroom couldn't have accommodated another single item. It was squeezed in with the proverbial shoehorn.

Suddenly it hit me! 'What am I doing? I've made the decision now, so I'll just have to go forward and see what unfolds.' After three months, I did move out to a flat of my own, my savings fast dwindling day by day. Reality struck me. I'd always lived in a decent area, respectable, but look at me now. Here I found myself in this horrible run- down place, where people appeared in shops in their dressing gowns and slippers. My kids thought I'd lost the plot! Nearby I discovered a Community Centre which also housed a library. I went there on a very regular basis. A wide variety of classes took place at the Centre like exercise and zumba, also ESOL and computer classes. In addition to my library visits, I started my new exercise regime plus computer classes once a week, tackling courses on Word and Excel. I worked at a charity shop and later graduated to a College H.N.D. course in Admin and IT. Inevitably my courses would come to an end. The next step in this chain of events arrived when I replied to an advert on Gumtree:

Summer Volunteer required for 3 months
PITLOCHRY

A job to do over the summer, I thought, as I would return to college to do Accountancy. At the age of 49 I had a determined streak in my personality. I had some sort of inner strength. I had drifted out of religion, but I remember praying.

I decided: 'Get up! Get on with your life!' I went to Pitlochry in

March for an interview. Iain, the manager, and Glynnis interviewed me. I remember it was a very relaxed interview. Over the next few months, I emailed them on two separate occasions just to confirm that their offer still held for the summer time. I wanted to make sure I was still going. I was nervous, not a teenager. How would I manage with all that, living and working in the same place? It was a shock at first. The last time I'd been in a similar situation was 30 years ago when I worked at Butlins.

When I arrived and started the staff were so supportive and caring people. All good things come to an end though. The three months was up and I got a housekeeper's job in a local hotel which was a whole contrasting scenario. It was a different environment. I had numerous rooms to clean by 2pm. Impossible! I stayed in grotesque staff quarters. Needless to say I was very unhappy. I rebelled. I walked out; returned to the Atholl Centre in tears and pleaded for help. Miraculously, their Admin Assistant suddenly got a job elsewhere. I had an interview with two of the trustees and the Manager who asked me the MOST awkward questions!

He told me later that very day I HAD THE JOB!

After that my life was totally enriched by the people I met including disabled people, women on their own, local church people and foreign people. It happened by talking to them and doing my best.

My job also entails helping to cook food and serving meals. At the start I asked for training with this. Now I cook for people in the centre and I work at a house for elderly people – cooking their meals and MORE. I've made so many interesting friends here from different backgrounds and a wide variety of nationalities. I'm a stronger, more confident person. I don't sit back if things need to be done. Through it all, I've developed a whole new confidence and a range of new skills. I'm a different person. I had all the material things I could have needed in my former life but now I have a much richer life.

Getting up and doing what was necessary, learning all the way. A Happy Ending, but I've still loads of stuff to do!

Wilma Leighton

Wilma and her friends

Priceless

I live in a small place called Pitlochry the

view from the School is priceless it's of a

castle and a grand castle at that
The walls of stone are so old my dad says when

he was younger about my age sheep used to
wander into it and he'd do the same.

Pitlochry is good for a walk in the

Black

Spout woods even when it rains it's still
cheerful when
the
people walk by
you'll never be able to say good bye

Josh Cameron
Pitlochry Primary School

Pat's Story

I was born in the house called St Ann's on the Crieff Road in Aberfeldy.

In the year of 1947, when I was seven years old, we had a winter with bad snow. I remember going up to sledge at the Birks with a handmade sledge, made by Jimmy Small, who lived next door to us. The Crieff Road had been blocked by the snow at the Birks for about 6 weeks. We sledged down the main road as there was no traffic on it!

In my childhood there was a very special place in Aberfeldy. It was called 'The Happy Land' by the people who lived there because they all seemed so happy. There were wash houses at the back of the houses where everyone did their washing. Groups of girls, myself included, used to play in the station yard and the wash houses. We often played hide and seek. We didn't have the toys back then, nor the money to get them.

When I went to Dull School we all had a tin mug which we hung on our own peg on the wall. This was for our milk, which came in a big can and was left at the Cross in Dull. Two school children went and collected it and brought it to the school every day.

Pat Edward

Children sledging on the Crieff Road in Aberfeldy

The Big Tree Country

To visit Perthshire it's nice to play

But it's even nicer as a place to stay

You will have a great time

Stopping at the villages on the A9

There's Bankfoot, Birnam and Dunkeld

Pitlochry, Aberfeldy and the rest

The mountains, rivers and the lochs in summer at their best

Proud Schiehallion with its mountain peak

I'm lost for words, I cannot speak

It stands out above the rest

To climb it is a formidable test

The Loch of the Lowes ospreys come again

Hoping their brood will hatch again

The Stone of Destiny is located at Scone

To crown the kings of Scotland

The stone belongs to us not England

Loch Tay runs into the River Tay

How many salmon are caught each day

The bright white façade of Blair Castle

The stags lock horns to do their battle

There's the Birks at Aberfeldy

It's a pleasant walk when the sun shines brightly

The little birds sing their songs

Spring is here she can't be wrong

Hoping her brood will come along

To give them life and to hear their song

Spend a night in the forest

To hear the dawn chorus

There's the beech hedge at Blairgowrie

The tallest in Europe, it's worth a bounty

The oldest yew tree at Fortingall church

Where Pontius Pilate slept

It's a secret that's very well kept

At the Hermitage on the A9

Where the Black Linn Falls are sublime

At Huntingtower Mary Queen of Scots

Spent her wedding night,

married to Henry Stuart, Lord Darnley

She was wed three times

She liked wedding cake and apple bramley

Perthshire is the place to be

Steeped in all its history

Life is but a moment long

But love lasts forever in a song

Ian Petrie

Highland Perthshire - An Assault To The Senses

We take a lot of things in life for granted. The seasons come and go offering their miracles and we witness it all with our senses that for most of us are automatic. When we stop and take note we discover that the world around us bombards our senses with constant delight and experiences.

In springtime nature is waking up from its winter slumber, new colours appear and the sleepy landscape starts to put on a new wardrobe. Most of us notice the snowdrops first, their pale delicate emergence signalling that we are breaking out of winter's grip, ironically covering the ground with a white blanket. As the days move on and rising temperatures give us hope, daffodils appear as golden yellow trumpets heralding that spring is well and truly here. As spring progresses the bluebells surface as a river of colour cascading through the forest floor. The trees too are waking from their hibernation as silver birch leaves appear as tiny diamond shaped kites fluttering in the wind, a bright translucent green. From now on all sorts of trees are unfurling foliage like flags in the breeze. On the magnificent horse chestnut the blooms decorate the canopy like huge pink and white ice cream cones.

As the year marches on we await the alarm call of the cuckoo echoing across the hills and it signals a distinct time in the year. For many of us next in the calendar is the return of the swallows, these brave little fighter jets returning year in, year out to raise their young. As time goes by they are joined by the martins and swifts all here for the same reason. As spring becomes summer the swallows practise their aerial acrobatics with frightening precision, they are the ultimate in flight. I love listening too, to the swifts as they fly in groups around the rooftops with their unmistakeable distinctive screech.

Through spring and summer the weather is as weather does in Highland Perthshire. The sun pokes its head out on regular occasions through the many different types of rain we experience here. All this weather gives way to the bracken as it unfurls from tiny saplings to flapping triffids covering the ground in an almost impenetrable blanket. The damp also produces the vibrant colours we see in the mosses and lichens, my particular favourite. Along the roadside the broom is a yellow explosion of colour, like a firework across the sky. As you travel around throughout the year you are struck by how the bluebells, gorse, broom and finally heather create nature's patchwork quilt across the hills and glens, a staccato profusion of colour. The burns and streams rise and fall with the weather gurgling, bubbling or gushing in its amber peat colour. Viewing Loch Rannoch every day is a treat, as every day it is different. There are those magical days when all is calm and the water is flat and it reflects a mirror image of the landscape above. I relish the early morning light as the breeze gently ripples the water in the golden morning sun. Throughout the day and in each day we see the water take on many colours and guises.

Before we know it summer gives way to autumn. Many people view this as a sad time as everything starts to die back and yet this is my favourite time of year when you get those mornings where the mist hangs with the cool air with the loose promise of sunshine later in the day. I feel it is nature's technicolour fanfare, its last huge celebration before snuggling down for its winter hibernation. It starts slowly with the odd leaf here and the edges of bracken there and then the green gives way to a russet spectacular. The red squirrels blend in as they scurry through the undergrowth bobbing about like bouncy balls before disappearing up a tree. On our way to school we often pass this buzzard sitting on a telegraph pole and he peers down at us especially on dreich smirry rain days when he wears his wings like an overcoat. The geese alert us to the changing seasons as they fly in formation across the sky and soon the osprey and swallows will follow suit, searching out the warmth to enjoy their vacation. As we progress and the nights are drawing in the owls converse amongst the treetops and then the air comes alive with the prehistoric sound of the stags as they roar across the hills, voice battling voice; this is *their* hill. These proud, shy, majestic creatures blend in perfectly with their coarse red brown coats complementing the copper tones of autumn.

Autumn colours come and go and the flora and fauna settle into their winter sleep. The air changes and frost touches everything with a magical beauty. Every blade of grass, branch and spider's web sparkle like crystal dewdrops in the sunlight. The sky becomes a watercolour wash of many colours casting an ethereal light across the landscape. The snows come and go and come back again bringing joy to some, and hard work to others. The air is cold and sharp filling our lungs with the winter's day. Before we know it we've gone past the shortest day and the cycle is ready to start again.

What we see every day is nature's canvas as the weather and wildlife constantly change, shape and evolve the landscape providing us with nature's cinema.

Nicola Hannen

Loch Rannoch in its autumn glory

A Young Boy

My story and difficulties began when I was a young boy and my parents divorced. This caused me nightmares which were recurring and based around where I lived. I found it difficult to cope with these, often getting up in the middle of the night which resulted in disturbed sleep.

At school I had difficulties concentrating and behaviour issues. I firmly believe that I had Attention Deficit Hyperactivity Disorder (ADHD) which was never dealt with. As the behaviour got worse my parents decided to discipline me with a heavy hand which resulted in me rebelling and starting to take drugs; at the age of eight. I began by smoking cannabis. By the time I was sixteen I had taken most drugs that were on the streets including LSD, heroin, cocaine, speed, ecstasy and prescription drugs. I still smoke cannabis today but have given up the rest of them, even alcohol.

When I was sixteen I left home, I had a flat and my own business; life was great! At a party one night it all changed. I took four acid tablets and three ecstasy tablets which ended up with me having a serious breakdown. As a result I started to receive paranoid messages from the television and psychotic episodes including hallucinations with suicidal thoughts. The stress of being self-employed, drug taking and a close family member dying caused me to have a mental breakdown. The business went bust and I found myself with nothing; no money, no possessions and was I locked up in a mental institution.

The first time I was in the hospital was the scariest. I didn't know what to expect and I spent six months there. I was diagnosed with drug-induced psychosis. I was put on injections which were slow release and which were administered in the hip. These injections were sore and humiliating and left me wondering - after two years of them every fortnight - if I could do without them. I was still taking a lot of drugs at the time but I stopped these injections and it wasn't long before I was re-admitted.

I had eight admissions over that time. The longest was two years in a psychiatric forensic unit. In total I've spent about five years in the hospital altogether but I've been out for three years and I now feel confident enough to write my story.

My recovery has been long and slow and I feel like I've been bouncing from pillar to post. Entering the ward isn't the hardest part; that's at the end trying to prove to a psychiatrist that you're mentally well enough to live at home in the community.

This illness (Schizo Effective Disorder) has torn my family apart. It has left me a shadow of the boy they once knew. My parents always stuck by me in and out of hospital. I wish I hadn't wasted my youth and achieved something but when you're young you don't listen and think you are indestructible! Getting older and more mature has helped me accept my illness. I've looked back at my past and still feel guilty for worrying my family. Now I listen to their advice and my psychiatrist's along with the rest of the team. Anybody who has my illness and similar conditions should take medication and listen to the advice given by family and the health professionals.

I don't believe I'll ever be drug-free and my psychiatrist has explained that I'll be on medication for the rest of my life but I'm happy to be out of hospital and out living in the community. I feel lucky that I've managed to stay out for a few years now. I have finally found a balance with my medication allowing me to live my life normally with very few side effects.

Since I've had this illness I've helped to overcome it by keeping busy. I take part in regular exercise by going to the gym, playing football and walking. Other practices that keep me well are washing regularly and using breathing exercises as well as having a healthy diet and drinking lots of water and avoiding alcohol. It's important you feel confident in what you eat, how you look and what you do. Try not to let anything stand in your way. Having discipline has been good for me and it's helped me overcome anxiety about going into shops and not being paranoid to walk about with others without having panic attacks.

I hope you've liked my story. If it's any help to you then I'm satisfied. Maybe you should write your own story and it might help someone else to understand the battle that people with mental difficulties go through on a daily basis?

Steven Kay

An Experiment Gone Wrong

One Sunday afternoon, a number of years ago, my Mum went out to get her washing in from the line when she heard crackling sounds from her stick shed............ About 5 minutes later, lo and behold, the whole shed was ablaze!

Earlier on my brother, then aged 10, had come into the house, unbeknown to her, to collect matches and subsequently carried out a little boy's "experiment". The shed went up in flames on this particularly windy day. All the surrounding trees caught fire. Swiftly, Mum phoned the fire service and the police. My Dad, a part time Special Police Constable at the time, raced to the scene and commented to the constable in charge that he thought that Margaret, his wife, had put the chimney up on fire.

My brother came up the drive, wondering where the smoke was coming from, only to realise it was the result of his actions.

'Oh my goodness!'

Surrounded by flashing lights all around the place, it looked like a scene from 'London's Burning'. My Dad soon realised that his wife had nothing to do with the shenanigans after all. My brother Craig had a lot of explaining to do to my Mum and Dad. Obviously, he thought that his little experiment had been extinguished at the time (a quick stamp on the floor where he had set the 'little fire' in amongst some straw and kindling).

After a few hours everything was under control. It had taken thousands of gallons of water to put out the inferno. Also it was lucky that the wind was blowing in the other direction that day or it could easily have been more serious, as the house was only a few feet away from the scene. The only thing that remained hot for a while was a certain person's backside. I think he learned his lesson after that!

Debbie Maxtone

The Evacuees

Seventy-five years ago on the 3 September 1939, my brother Robert and I arrived in Aberfeldy as evacuees on the train from Glasgow. My brother was six, I was five. From what I am told, we boarded the train at Parkhead Station in Glasgow's East End. We arrived in Aberfeldy and were taken to a collection point at Breadalbane Academy. We were chaperoned by schoolteachers. After some time we were collected by Mr and Mrs Kininmonth from Duntuim Farm. They were known to us from then on as Mr and Mrs K. I seem to remember we were among the last to be collected. I think perhaps we were younger than they expected. Most of the evacuees went to Moness House and some were placed with families. Can you imagine being landed with two Glasgow vacs?

A few days after we arrived the food for the hens was spread on the grass outside the farmhouse, when the wild pigeons came down to take their share, I apparently asked — 'Do they belong to you too?' One day when I was about ten I was raking about in the workshop, which I loved doing. The ploughman Duncan (Dochie) Fraser had been there doing some work, when he left I went in. Shortly afterwards I heard footsteps on the stairs. I quickly jumped up into the rafters. Mr K entered and looked around, he spotted Dochie's half bottle of whisky sitting on the workbench, he went to the door and furtively looked around; returning to the bench he opened the bottle and took a quick slug. He was a teetotaler!

There are no words to fully describe how good the Kininmonths were to us. Mrs K was so gentle and kind. She was a qualified nurse having served in World War One. Mr K was a joiner and cabinet maker. He enjoyed passing on his skills to me, which I have put to good use. He had some wonderful sayings like: 'When they've a' been to university who's going to pu' the neeps?' They fed us and clothed us and sat us at the table with them for meals. For children from a poor background it was an adventure.

My job on the farm was the hen man. I collected the eggs, cleaned the henhouses and reported any hens which were poorly. I also made sure that there were enough kindlings for the fire. My brother worked with all the livestock. On Sunday nights Mr Mitchell the minister came up to Duntuim to play Monopoly. He dressed all in black with knee-length shiny boots. He scared the life out of me. If we met in the street I ran away. I enjoyed going with Jack to deliver the milk and eggs to the customers in Aberfeldy. The highlight of my day was going to Menzies the Baker in Kenmore Street with my pocket money to buy Paris buns, two for a penny. Yum yum! I still visit Jack – the K's' son - in care in Aberfeldy. He is now ninety-three. Sometimes after the evening milk delivery, my brother and I would go to see a picture at the Birks Cinema. It's nice to have it back in operation.

In 1943 my father visited Duntuim. I ran away and hid, thinking he was there to take me back to Glasgow. We stayed at Duntuim until May 1945. At that point, with the war in Europe over, we had to return to our parents in Glasgow. After three very unhappy weeks there, we returned to Duntuim and remained there until May 1947 when Mr K retired from the farm. I returned to Glasgow, to Linthouse in Govan, while my brother went to work at Crofness Farm. He remained there for a year then returned to Glasgow. In June 1950, having returned to Aberfeldy, I first worked at Borlick, Killiechassie, then at Balintyre, Glenlyon. How lucky to live in the glen. I remained in the district until I went to the army in March 1952.

Mr &. Mrs Kininmonth did not need to take us in - they did. They did not need to be good to us - they were. I consider it the happiest of circumstances. They were both a great influence on my life and I think it appropriate that I should say so. My wife and I are still regular visitors to the Aberfeldy district and the Kininmonth family. Perthshire is a beautiful county. The daughter Cecilia (Cecily) Kininmonth was in the WRNS during the war, while the son John Alastair (Jack) stayed on the farm. We attended Breadalbane

Academy. Part of the Town Hall was requisitioned as classrooms because of the extra numbers. Jack's family, Elizabeth and Alastair, are still our very close friends, indeed they are family. After my own children were born Mr and Mrs K became Grandad & Granny Glen. When I had leave from the army I headed for Tomnacroich to see them, sometimes staying for a few days.

Tom Gilmour

4 Dunkeld Walks in Verse

All it requires is open eyes and stout boots. Start moving and the path reveals itself

The Stank, Birnam Glen

Across mica-ed rock
pinpricks of sunlit bubbles
trail the surface -
a flotilla of comets heading to the
edge of a known galaxy
to move towards sluice gates
now defunct - on rust up bolt
the foundry name two centuries intact -
then narrowing
from the water's defined bowl
to launch into a pool below,
a black hole,
a bolt of tawny silk
spilling over the weir, then
frothing into light ale.
Fists of ferns starfish the bank.
Once, discarded on the pebbly beach,
a pair of child's socks
patterned with flying saucers,
astronauts.

The Rocking Stone

Surfing a tide of green
to the blue of the hill horizon,
marooned,
beached inland,
harbouring amid a sea of larches
is a petrified whale
dorsal fin and eye -
sightless up into Atholl -
skin calloused, rough
to brush like oyster shell,
jaw on a ball of frozen schist.
On the left flank
a heart carved into flesh
of stone.

Poets' Path

There was some talk about
which path to take
the best route to the top.
The needle dittered, settling
in one direction then another.

Viewing the moor and hill ahead
from the cover of the trees,
soft rasp of wind in bracken,
and topmost branches of a fir
jiggling a highland fling,
we strung out like a hefted flock
to file the old familiar roads
only to find that we had somehow
got it wrong, were lost,
the compass point, pointless.

The muse when consulted,
smiled, said nothing,
and on her lap a grey cat
licked his paws and purred
deep from within.

*paths are where we come to know ourselves and others who may
have stepped a similar way.*

Upper Newtyle Beat

the gillies hut is a trig wee howf
its pinted blue and rid
its made o wid wi a bench and lum
and a roof o corrugated

whiles it wiz the gowfers' shiel
until they bigged anither
But noo its braw fer the fishermen
tae hirsel in the gither

the ghillie foreby's a couthy lad
who kens the river weel
whit pool tae cast or croy tae staund
whit fly tae use or reel

athort fra'a crag they ca' Doo's Nest
on sooth bank o the Tay
alang the Terrace tae sandy straund
ye'll ee it on stravaig

Mary McDougall

A Huge Adventure – A First for Me

My story is about a recent trip to Belfast with two friends from the Atholl Centre in Pitlochry, where I do regular Volunteering. One day when I was in the office, I asked Wilma what she was doing. She replied: 'If I told you what I was doing, I would be revealing a TOP SECRET!' So I left it. The next few days went by. Then she asked me, 'Do you want to come on a holiday with me and Michal?' 'Why not?' I responded. I was so excited as we booked our flights and our hotel accommodation in Belfast. This was a first for me. I'd never been on a holiday to another country without my Mum and Dad.

I had three weeks to wait and I drove them both mad! Couldn't shut up! Slowly those three weeks went by. Finally, at the Atholl Centre, Wilma was ready. I helped her by lifting up her case. It was SO heavy. I told her I thought there must be a body in it! She was all ready to go and I went home that night to get some sleep as we were leaving at 6 o'clock the next morning. In the morning, my Dad gave us all a lift to Edinburgh Airport. Michal, the most sensible one of our trio, checked his small bag in first, and there was no excess charge. 'Lucky lad!' I thought. Wilma's turn next, after she dragged her case from the entrance across the airport, bitterly complaining of sore arms! She wasn't so lucky: the woman announced: 'That'll be £50 please!' Then my turn. '£30 to pay.'

We made our way to Security and Passport Control. Michal and Wilma went in one queue while I went in another. Too late I realized that somehow our bags were now mixed up. Accidentally I had charge of Wilma's hand baggage! Thinking that if I might be asked if I had packed this bag, I'd have to say 'yes.' Thank goodness security trusted me! I must have an honest face! The beeper sounded as I walked through the scanner. I was searched and was instructed to take off my shoes. The other two were already through and stood amused as I was sweating buckets. By the time I succeeded in joining them at the other side and retrieved my bags the next disaster unfolded as I spotted my shoes travelling round and round the conveyor belt. I got them and we made our way to the plane. I was already shaken, and fell flat on my face, nearly taking Michal with me as we went up the stairs to board. At last we found our seats, belted up and the pilot prepared to make his way down the runway for take off. I thought to myself 'Thank God!' It felt as though it had taken all day to get to this stage. We'll be in Belfast soon. Yippee! Just at that moment, however, there was a loud noise. It was like the plane had died. Michal looked at me and I looked at him and both said 'This can't be happening!' Then there was an announcement from the Captain: 'We have a slight technical problem. We'll need to get it seen to.' We were stuck on the runway with nowhere to go: kids screaming in the background, people moaning and a hot and stuffy atmosphere.

About one and a half hours later we were up in the air and then finally arrived at Belfast Airport. As we got off, I asked Wilma about the location of our hotel. Apparently, it was only a short journey away in the city centre. So we collected our cases and headed for the bus. On arriving at the city centre, Wilma asked the driver where our hotel was. 'Oh, that's on the other side of the city,' was his reply. I couldn't believe it! So we headed for ANOTHER long adventure. Just as well my case has wheels on it!

Some time later we eventually arrived at the hotel, which was very nice: right by the water and the Titanic Museum, which we planned to visit. Very handy and it all looked amazing. That night outside the museum, the surrounding area was floodlit with blue and green LED lights to simulate the shape of the ship. Michal just sat there within this shape as Leonardo De Caprio would have done in the Titanic film. It seemed like I was watching it on TV. Somehow unreal!

The next day, we went into the Titanic Exhibition and walked round led by our guide. It was very well done. He was very helpful and informative. We saw some amazing displays like the ship's drawing room, followed by a ride which explained what jobs the crew did, what it was like to be a passenger on the Titanic and also about their families. Then after our guided tour we took some time to go around again ourselves just to take it all in. It was so good that we spent the whole day there. I loved it all. I think we were the last people to leave that day because we found it so interesting. We did have a disaster in the middle of the day when we went to sit down for a break and a bite to eat. I heard this cracking sound from my back pocket. Too late, I realized my phone was smashed; all the photos that I took were lost. I was so upset as I had taken lots and lots of interesting shots during the tour which I had saved to my phone instead of the SIM card. Utterly disastrous! However, on a good note, it was a fantastic holiday shared with such great friends!   I will never forget it and I would recommend if you haven't been to see the Titanic Exhibition it's well worth making the effort.

I hope you have enjoyed my story. I can't wait to do one next year, as I can write about my holiday in Poland where I am going in a week's time on 3 December 2014 to see my best buddy Michal who is now back living in his home country of Poland.

David Caldwell

Wilma, Michal and David outside Titanic exhibition in Belfast

Pitlochry

The first time I heard about the Highlands was in 1998, when my older brother went to spend two months to a little town in the middle of Scotland, called Pitlochry. I'm from Spain, so that sounded to me far, far away. In 2011 and 2013 I had the opportunity to spend my summer too in that precious town, working as volunteer in the Atholl Centre. During my stay there, I used to go in my days off to explore the Highlands. I have to say that the first thing I did when I arrived was go to the tourist office to take a map of walk paths of the area.

One day I had the day off, and I decided to go up to the top of the Ben Vrackie mountain. I remember that the closer I got to the mountain, the more fog was on the top, and I was thinking that it would be impossible to go to my goal. But suddenly, just when I arrived to the lake that is in front of Ben Vrackie, the sun started to shine like it was showing me the path and saying me 'come on, you can go on'. If you have been on the top of that mountain, it's not necessary to explain what you can see and feel there. If you have not been there, and you have the opportunity, you must go. It's like being on the top of the world.

When I went down, I decided to follow the path to Killiecrankie. My map of walk paths said that the path was well signed. But, maybe I don't have the same concept of 'well signed'. The fact is that I was in the middle of the land, surrounded by sheep that were looking at me like I was the first human who they saw in months. But I had to continue on my way! And from time to time I saw the sign of the path (a little man in green pointing the right way). It's curious, but I like to compare life with those kind of walk paths. Sometimes you feel lost, you don't know if you are on the right way, but when you see a signal (a signal that you don't know who put it or when it was put there) you only can do an act of faith and follow it.

I finally arrived at the pass of Killiecrankie, a very peaceful place to take a rest on my way. But the day was not going to finish yet. I had to come back to Pitlochry, so I took the path along the River Garry. But when I was in the Faskally Wood, I lost myself... again! I could not find a sign to continue the path. When I started to feel nervous, a forest guard suddenly appeared behind a tree. Really! He asked me if I was lost, and I told him that I was trying to go to Pitlochry, so the guard said to me 'Don't worry, I will go with you and I'll show you the path'. So we were together for a time, speaking about Spain and Scotland, and when we were near the Clunie Bridge, the guard said goodbye to me. I arrived safely to my beloved town, and when my boss saw me entering through the door he asked 'Hi Amaia! Did you enjoy your day off?' And I could only crack a smile and answer 'Really, It has been an awesome day!'

So here am I now, dear diary, in a pub with a pint of beer, writing you all my adventures. Who knows, maybe some day someone will read it and be encouraged to explore without fear of getting lost on the paths of the Highlands...

Amaia Alcalde Gimilio

The Musings of Haggis John

I am originally from Bristol. I moved to Pitlochry in February of 2012. I've been made very welcome by numerous people. Together with other authors I was involved in the awesome project which resulted in the publication of a book entitled *Life As We Know It*. It's available in Highland Perthshire libraries.

I'm currently a walk leader and have enjoyed the company of many folk who relate stories of their lives and the history of Pitlochry. I'm now known by many nicknames here. For example *McWurzel* in McKays where we enjoy hospitality on Sunday evening with music jam sessions. And, yes, I sing scrumpy and western songs! I'm also known as *Pipesmoker* at the Old Mill where I have been made very welcome indeed. Ask them about the bloke who says 'WUNDERBAR' when his pint or real ale arrives. Another alias is *Haggis John* at both Moreton's and Hetties. My concerns relating to settling here have vanished. Everywhere everyone is cheerful and caring. A classic example is Hugh at the chippy. He raises fantastic sums of money for various charities and local organisations.

Some folk say there is nothing to do. I reply there is and just look at notices or listen to information on the excellent Heartlandfm radio station and ENJOY. If you see me out and about please have a chat and a bit of banter.

John Henley

Connections

Occasionally I visit a friend in London who I met at college: she was 7 or 8 years older than me, well travelled and well educated. She lent me books on world literature and generally advised me. Perhaps I should say argued against my small town mindset. Nobody read Maxim Gorky or Tolstoy in my street.

She has recently published a book of short stories – I had already read one of them, about Isaac Rosenberg, a very important World War One poet. It was an imagined reconstruction of an incident from his boyhood in Bristol. Noticing the biography of Rosenberg she had used for information, I flipped through it for pictures – a lot of self portraits (as an aspiring artist he couldn't afford to pay sitters) and any done of his comrades he obviously gave to them. Suddenly I saw a name which took me straight home to Fortingall – Molteno, Betty Molteno and a friend, in South Africa. Surely a relation of the Molteno family that used to live in Glenlyon House.

Betty Molteno was in the book because she tried to help Rosenberg to get commissions when he was in South Africa in 1914, and even gave him accommodation in her own home. He was too homesick for Whitechapel and the Slade School of Art. As he wrote to a friend in London, when he put his shoes, soles full of holes, out to be polished to a patent-leather gloss, he felt too fraudulent to write or paint, so he came back home and joined up – bandy, terrible lungs, five foot two and a half tall, always in jankers for not keeping his mind on the job, his brain always thinking about painting or writing. He was killed on the Arras-St Quentin front on the first of April 1918, his body never recovered.

This Betty Molteno, headmistress of the leading girls school in the Cape, was also a friend of Mahatma Ghandi, and was the daughter of Sir John Molteno, the first Prime Minister of Cape Colony. Like all the family, she tried to make peace between Britain and the Boers, but also believed in votes for black and coloured South

Africans. Her brother Percy pioneered the transport of refrigerated fruit from the family farm to Britain, and this brought him in contact with Sir Donald Currie of the Union Castle Line. Percy married Sir Donald's daughter Elizabeth, and became MP for Dumfriesshire. The Moltenos inherited the Glenlyon estate, and after their death in 1935 and 36 the Molteno Memorial Hall was erected in Fortingall to their memory. I would like to think that there is also room in the glen for a remembrance of Isaac Rosenberg. Perhaps one of his poems, which his sister collected from his letters home, and which influenced Modernists like Ezra Pound and T S Eliot....

> Through these pale, cold days
> What dark faces burn
> Out of three thousand years,
> And their wild eyes yearn.
> While underneath their brows
> Like waifs their spirits grope
> For the pools of Hebron again –
> For Lebanon's summer slope.
> They leave these blond still days
> In dust behind their tread
> They see with living eyes
> How long they have been dead.

(sent to his friend Edward Marsh on 28th March 1918)

Rosie Hooper

Glen Tilt of International Fame

Highland Perthshire has so much of beauty and of interest to share. Glen Tilt and the track over the hills to the Linn of Dee not only give great pleasure to many local people, to hikers and cyclists, but perhaps most especially to geologists who come from all around the world to make somewhat of a pilgrimage there.

It is at GlenTilt that James Hutton, 'the father of modern geology' found the proof to confirm his belief that granite rocks had once been molten. The evidence of this can be seen particularly clearly about five miles up the glen where the road passes a small wood and runs parallel to the quiet waters of the Tilt where their pattern changes to tumble over a waterfall between the rocks.

In scientific circles in the late 1700s, arguments were often raging about the ultimate origins of granite and related igneous rocks. While James Hutton was formulating his book *"Theory of the Earth"* many hotly disputed explanations were circulated about how all the rocks on the face of the Earth had been formed. On the one hand, the German mineralogist, Abraham Gottlieb Werner, proposed that a 'universal' ocean had once blanketed the Earth and that all rocks were deposited from this primeval water-world. To give added credibility to Werner's ideas, biblical references readily accommodated Noah's Flood along with strong echoes from the Book of Genesis.

The rocks at Glen Tilt proved to be one of the key sites in settling this debate. Hutton, despite the difficulties of travel in the late 18th century, went out of his way to search throughout Scotland to find a location where the edge of a granite body was exposed. He found that evidence in the riverbed at Glen Tilt. There to their great delight, Hutton and his field companion and artist, John Clerk of Eldin, noted 'the granite breaking and displacing the strata in every conceivable manner'. In other words, the veins of granite had clearly intruded and penetrated the older rocks. This demonstrates a key principle – that the granite had been in a molten state when it was introduced into the surrounding rock. Hutton's discovery then opened the way to the systematic study of the geology of Scotland.

If you would like to learn more of Hutton's discoveries – and much more - I recommend the little book by my late husband Donald B. McIntyre and Alan McKirdy: *'James Hutton, The Founder of Modern Geology'* published by the National Museum of Scotland, Edinburgh, and also the beautiful *'Land of Mountain and Flood – The Geology and Landforms of Scotland'* by Alan McKirdy, John Gordon and Roger Crofts, published by Birlinn Limited.

Ann I McIntyre

Ann's husband Donald in Glen Tilt consulting John Clerk's drawings of 1785

My Scottish Adventure

Hi, my name is Michal. I am 33 years old and I am from The Czech Republic. I would like to tell you the story of my Scottish adventure. My goal is to show other people a simple example of what you can achieve if you are not afraid of hard work and if you want to follow your dreams.

It all started in the summer of 2005. I got an idea to go abroad for a longer time than just for holidays. I asked Markéta (my girlfriend) what she thought about that and she surprisingly answered "yes, I would go too". So it gave me a bit of courage to make things happen. It was not an easy decision because both of us had a good job (I was an accountant and Markéta was a teacher), we had been living in a lovely flat and having a nice life. Actually there was no need to make such a big change but that time I just felt it was the right decision to do. So we handed our notice in, moved out all the stuff from our flat and got ready for a new experience with a life abroad.

We wanted to go to an English speaking country so we chose London at the beginning. But when we started to look for a job we found that it was quite hard if you are not there. But in the end we were quite lucky. We found an advert on the internet saying that someone was looking for waiting staff at a place called Motorgrill in Ballinluig. We found Ballinluig is a Scottish village in a region called Perthshire. We just thought it could be good so we phoned and in a week's time we started to work there. It was a really quick move but in the end I think it was maybe better for us because we did not have much time to think about it.

That time I did not know how good it was for us to get to Scotland. At the beginning it was a bit difficult for us. New country, culture, people, language, habits etc. It was really hard; especially for me because I did not speak any English when we came (Markéta did so she was fine). I felt like a small child; nobody understood me and I did not understand anybody. Fortunately I was very lucky and found the Community Learning Centre in Pitlochry. In the learning centre I discovered an English course for foreign people. That was the place where I met one of the most important people in my life. I met Pam McDonald. This nice, charming, energetic and always helpful lady influenced my life so much. It was so interesting to watch her every lesson how she tried to teach us, show us and tell us as much as possible. She taught me the language and showed me the right direction, how to use the language and how to live in Scotland. It was so fascinating to watch our progress every week and I was so glad I could be part of that. Thanks to Pam and the course I was able to work and live for years in my second homeland.

Back to our job. As I said we started in place called Motorgrill. We worked as waiting staff there and after so many years I have to say it was the best option for us to take. It gave me not only the time to learn basic habits in the country but also to improve my English. Clive, the owner of that place, is such a gentleman. I have never had such a good and caring employer before. He helped us so much during our stay with different things, protected us from rude people and mainly gave us the first chance to work abroad. We are very indebted to him and it was the reason why we worked there such a long time. So I hope we managed to give him a bit back. Apart from our full-time job we had a part-time job too. It was in a hotel called Craigvrack. We went through all kinds of hotel jobs there during all the years and later on we had a chance to be involved in running that place too. I would like to mention Alan and Barbara, the owners, who trusted us and gave us a chance to try something new and different. Having two jobs kept us pretty busy but we were glad because we were never been bored and every year we got closer to our dream to make money for building our own house.

Apart from hard work we managed to do many more pleasant things too. We have done lots of travelling there and managed to see nearly the whole country and most of the islands. We met a lot of local people but also met so many people from other countries all over the world and it gave us a chance to make many friendships. I would like to mention other people who entered into our lives. Bill and Barbara (our landlords) who made us to feel in their home as in our home. Our friend Babs who showed us a different point of view on our life. I have to mention Murray, my football coach, who always kept an eye on me and was giving me a chance to escape from hardworking reality every week. I would mention all my football mates, local people, our guests and customers because they were just fantastic to us and gave us an unforgettable time in Scotland. If someone says the name of the country I always remember beautiful countryside, friendly people and years of living without worries.

At the end of my story I would like to encourage all the people who are thinking about going abroad to start new life or just want to try something new. Just go for it because there will not be another chance in your life!!! And I have to say it is really worth it to do that. It gave me so much. I got a great experience (can compare living in different countries), a knowledge of new language, made many new friends, made our dream come true (earned money for our house), encouraged us to keep on travelling and see other countries like New Zealand or Australia, opened new possibilities in our future lives etc. So my last words will be dedicated to all people who made Scotland our second home!!!!! Thanks a lot for everything you have done for us. We will never forget !!!!!

Michal Blazej

Kirkmichael

Oor village is braw, wi nae hassle at aw
Awbidy seems calm and contentit
Wi heilan coos in a herd, or a twitterin bird
There's naethin tae get fowk dementit

Teachers follow the rule, at oor local school
Where the bairns are aw happy and glad
Yon pupils start singin, when they hear the bell ringin
An not wan is doonherted or sad

We hiv jist the wan shop, but it's got the lot
Milk, tatties, cream cakes by the dozen
Come in spend yer money, they've even got honey
Fir each day it's fair cheery an buzzin

Aye, it's a pity, but ye can keep yir big city
Wi voices aw rantin and ravin
Jist gie me this life, wi nae bother or strife
As this place is a wee bit like heaven

Elaine Mutch

Daniel Robertson of Dalnaglar

Like many folk, I wander down to the cemetery in lower Crieff to pause by the graves of the departed, to wonder at what they must have been like to know personally. Tallest of all the granite monuments there is one dedicated to a Daniel Robertson. The sad sight of some of the stones, which once were set against the base, lying forlorn on the ground as a path edging. But the inscription tells of a man who was much loved and respected in the community, and who was honoured by the generosity of local Strathearn people who contributed to this impressive monument.

Daniel was born at Clathic House, between Crieff and Comrie, in about 1803 and was educated at the Comrie school. He was clearly an intelligent boy, with a mass of curly brown hair, energetic and with aspirations to become a lawyer. Having gone some way along this path he found that the profession was 'overcrowded' and turned to banking as a career, first with the Commercial Bank then later with the Union Bank of Scotland. He obtained a high proficiency in accounting and soon found himself being promoted to inspector of branches; he was not yet 30 years old. In 1834 the recently formed National Provincial Bank in London wanted to recruit a vigorous and experienced 'Scotsman' to become their first General Manager. The list of applicants was a formidable 115 candidates. Daniel secured the position.

Why should a brand new joint stock bank based in London search for a Scotsman? The answer; because the English did not know how to run a bank! In the 20 years previously, 230 English banks had collapsed, with depositors losing their savings and causing ruin to many businesses. In Scotland there were no failures in over 40 years! Before that Scotland had experiences of small banks which failed and the natural instinct of those who learned the lessons formed a set of practices which would provide the security the public wanted. One example can be illustrated by a small Crieff bank, situated in the street called Bank Street (of course!), by the entrance to the car park off Galvelmore Street today. This bank used to hold the deposits of many local folk and a good many farmers. One day they found that the manager/owner had absconded with their money. The scoundrel was never seen again! Having had such experiences Scotland took banking very seriously indeed. The English didn't!

It was this scenario that led a sculptor's son from Newcastle on Tyne to think big. In fact, to copy the Scottish model. His name was Thomas Joplin. With the support of a number of wealthy businessmen and landowners, Joplin founded the National Provincial Bank. It was not without problems, as one would expect, but eventually a stable Board of Directors was appointed. It would be too much here to go into all that Daniel achieved in the 30 years at the helm; suffice to say the Bank prospered.

Here are some of the highlights of his tenure:

Half day working on Saturdays to allow employees time for recreation and exercise
A pension plan for employees (a first for any business in the country)
Financial provision for widows
For exceptional (!) endeavours on behalf of the Bank, a bonus of *not exceeding 10%* of annual salary was payable to managers.

Before heading south, Daniel had married a lady from Kirkcaldy. They had two sons and seemed a very happy couple. On one of their visits to Perthshire they bought an old farm house up Glenshee, a place called Dalnaglar. The farmhouse was redesigned to look like an old Highland castle, as was the fashion when Queen Victoria set eyes on the Highlands and bought Balmoral estate. About the same time, Daniel and the family built another home on the then outskirts of Crieff, and called this house Dalnaglar too. Today it is a Nursing Home.

As retirement approached, tragedy struck the family. Both his sons and his beloved wife died in an epidemic of flu (or maybe tuberculosis), and were buried in London. Daniel never lived at the 'castle' he built; he decided to live in his Crieff home.

However he never forgot his roots. With his exceptional skills at talking to landowners and wealthy people, he persuaded obstinate Laird Murray of Ochtertyre to allow a new road to be constructed between Crieff and Comrie: he suggested that the Laird be wise and grant the folk of Crieff a good quality water supply from Loch Turret to flow down to the town! This pleased the townsfolk, and the council, which resulted in the magnificent fountain in James Square. Murray was chuffed!

Daniel's benevolence was behind other projects instigated by the local council, but he gave strict instructions that his name would not appear anywhere as the source of the money. Many a local would have guessed that the lovely old man with the grey tousled hair under the 'lum hat' had something to do with these enterprises. Daniel died in 1866, at a friend's home in Edinburgh, and he is buried there.

The memorial in Crieff cemetery became his only identifiable mark in Crieff, and it is sad that it has deteriorated . The National Provincial Bank was swallowed up by the Royal Bank of Scotland many years ago.....I wonder if there's any chance they might contribute to its restoration? Too much to hope for perhaps?

David Tod

Daniel Robertson

Demonstrative Dementia

Hiding money,
Flagging down cars,
Jump on a jet plane;
Could end up in Mars,
Confused happy,
Chatty tatty,
If lucid be the word,
Maybe quite ratty,

Loves the dogs,
Loves the weans,
Loves her grub,
Love in chains,

Forget the time,
Don't know where you are,
Heart forget to beat,
Might walk too far,

Frightened by noise,
Heartbreak will lend,
Remember how clever,
Sometime will end!

Florence Fraill
(in memory of her mum)

My Mum

You were so special in so many ways,

I wish I had told you every single day,

I remember you with such fondness,

such a character it's true.....

you were my crazy moo!

Time has stood still and we are worlds apart

I hope when I'm gone we can go back to the start,

amend the rift that feels so silly now.

My little mum with such a personality

no one could ever have that much originality.

You will never be forgotten.

You are and always will be

MY MUM

Heather Fraill
(in memory of her mum, Florence)

Dunkeld and Birnam Reminiscences

In 1943 my parents took over two businesses in Dunkeld, one the ice cream and sweet shop and the other a café. I was four years old and my sister seven. My sister and I had to work in the shop and café from an early age; I was about seven when I started serving properly. My father put boxes for me to stand on behind the counter so that I could see over it. We had to go into the shop when we came home from school and also at weekends. We often had to ice cakes for the café before we went to school. My mother did all the baking for the café. Sweets were rationed and we had to take coupons for them. People were only allowed so many sweets per coupon. At the end of the day we had to count all the coupons. Boy Scouts and the Boys' Brigade used to come and camp in the village of Inver every summer and they used to come into the shop. Often the parents would come to Bed and Breakfast with us – it was the family holiday. We made friends with some of the families for many years. Most of them were from Dundee and Fife. Sometimes we had visits from a London Boys' Brigade. They had fife and drum bands and we used to love listening to them. My sister and I used to be invited to their camp fires; we thought we were so special!

* * *

I was involved with a very special project - to build an extension to the Birnam Institute. The new building is now called Birnam Arts. I was on the steering committee and it was the most wonderful learning project. It involved constant meetings and visiting professional people for help and advice. It was hard work getting the funding for it. There were a lot of tears and sleepless nights. It took many years but it was worth it. We got there in the end and it is a great asset to the village. It has also won awards. I was so proud to have a special interest in the project as my great grandfather, William Campbell, was involved in the building of the original Birnam Institute. His name is on the original account.

Rita Murray

Rita and her sister outside their shop with members of the London Boys' Brigade

Our Wee Spottie Dog

We were introduced to this little puppy by one of our neighbours and she asked if we would keep the pup. She was so adorable there was no choice! (The pup I mean.)

She was so small she fitted into my hand, which was OK but as the night wore on she seemed to be not so well. I decided to sit up with her, as I didn't want my children to find her if she didn't survive the night.

If you read on with this you'll find she survived OK and we had her for ten years. She was half Shetland Collie and half Spaniel and was born with the best of both breeds. We named her Brandy.

She was also cat friendly, which was just as well as we had some over the years. One of our cats had kittens and Brandy just adored them. She couldn't wait for Bomber (the mother) to leave them, she was in the box quick as a flash! She and Bomber also took the kittens for a walk as soon as they were old enough. It was like a procession – Bomber first, kittens next – then Brandy bringing up the rear! It was really nice to watch them.

On the other hand Brandy was a very good actress. If she thought she wasn't getting in the car with us, her head would droop and she did the very slow walk back into the house! All that was needed was to pick up her lead and she was out the house and in the car before the magic 'oh come on then' words had been said.

We really enjoyed her for the ten years we had her, tantrums and all.

Isobel Quinn

Brandy, Bomber and the family

Bomb in the Bog - Two Stories in One

German Junker bombers jettisoned unused bombs over the hills of Perthshire as they returned to base in Nazi occupied Norway during World War 2. On 6th April 1943 an unexploded mine landed in a wood on the hillside above the Edradour Distillery.

I was out with my parents on a lovely summer in 1980 for an afternoon walk and picnic to Loch Ordie in the hills above Tulliemet and Dunkeld. We were walking over a boggy area to the north of the loch when I noticed a conical metal cylinder sticking out of the ground. We went over to look at it and my father who had been in the navy during the war thought it was possibly a bomb as it also had official government looking markings round the rim. We left it well alone and it was decided that as soon as we arrived back in Pitlochry I should inform the local police.

The bomb disposal squad arrived with the Inspecting Ordnance Officer, Lieutenant Cronne, from their base at Murthly near Dunkeld to inspect the mine up at Edradour. He set explosives round the mine and the Bomb Squad took shelter 50 metres away by sheltering behind a stone dyke. The Ordnance Officer then pressed the plunger to set off the explosives.

I went to the Police Station in Pitlochry to report the possible bomb. A statement was given and they said I would be contacted once they had informed the relevant authorities. Local Police Sargeant Dougie McLaren came round to my house to take me up to Loch Ordie. He had to verify my statement so that he could report back to the Bomb Squad who were on standby at Edinburgh. He arrived in a brand new white Police Range Rover and off we went. He drove round by Dunkeld and up by Riemore Lodge so that he could inform Colonel Lylle of the situation. We then drove round by rough tracks to within walking distance of the suspected bomb in the bog. When we got there Sargeant McLaren had a good look at the tube of metal sticking out of the ground. For some unexplained reason he decided to take hold of the object and yank it out of the marsh.

The bomb blast at Edradour set off a massive explosion with tons of earth, rock and trees being blown high in the air. The stone wall which the men were sheltering behind saved then from any harm. A huge crater was made and is known locally as 'Cronne's Crater' named after Lt. Cronne. The shaken Bomb Squad were able to calm down with a wee drink at the Distillery.

A Police Officer arrived at my address to be met by my very white-faced mother. All he could say was that I was OK, not to worry but he had no further information to give to my concerned parents.

We arrived back at Riemore Lodge and Sargeant McLaren explained to the Laird what had happened. We got back into the Range Rover but the new vehicle just would not start no matter what Sargeant McLaren tried. He decided to radio for assistance and while we waited for rescue from the glen we retired to the big house with Colonel Lylle, his wife and his daughter to the drawing room. The Laird's wife organised tea and scones and even offered us a sherry which was politely declined, Sargeant McLaren being on duty of course. About an hour later a Police car arrived to pick us up while the Range Rover was left to be retrieved the following day. We were driven back to Pitlochry and home. I was able to explain to my anxious parents what had actually happened as by this time we had been away for hours.

Recently on a lovely autumn afternoon I walked up with Eddie Stewart of Knockbarry Farm to see the bomb crater above Edradour. The crater still clearly shows the size of the explosion and the potential damage that could have been done to Pitlochry if it had not been harmlessly dropped on the moor.

My dad had been a Medical Officer in the Royal Navy and had never examined a bomb - just ill patients. Col Lylle had made a bit of a fuss about my 'bomb' but Sargeant McLaren made it clear that all suspect objects should be reported after all the bombs that had been dropped in the area all those years ago. What Sargeant McLaren had pulled out of the ground turned out to have been a long forgotten official British, harmless, rain gauge.

Iain Walker

My Autumn Dream

A quiet autumnal morning
Everything peaceful and still
I slowly scanned my eyes along
The lovely Kenmore hill

I reached the tall white tower
That overlooks the scene,
When suddenly there is a change
That must surely be a dream

The trees are a blaze of colour
That is certain to impress,
I have never seen this lady
With a lovelier autumn dress

I've reached the end of my scan
As the air is turning cool,
And end my happy journey
Beside the Battery Pool

Now all the leaves have fallen
And the trees are tall and serene,
I know that deep inside my heart
I'll still have my autumn dream

DTB Curley

Lost Places

I love Perthshire. I have done since the summer morning in 1983 when I stepped off the sleeper in Pitlochry and made my way down to the dam, there being nothing else to do. There was nowhere open for breakfast. I had no reason to think so, but it felt like coming home (more than presumptuous as I was only there for a job interview.) Over the years I've worn out countless pairs of boots and retired several bikes. In my last job I had the good fortune to be in hiking boots and with a rucksack, looking forward to a day in the hills, thinking: 'it's gone 8.30 so I suppose I've just clocked on!' After more than a quarter of a century I thought I knew the place.

Then I had my eyes opened.

There are hidden ways to forgotten vistas, waterfalls and follies all across Highland Perthshire; lost places, if you like. Once oft-frequented (if only by the laird, his guests and ghillies), sometimes still worked over in the shooting season; but largely forgotten now, certainly by the guidebooks.

Who among us has stood on Elrick More, and looked down on Loch Skiach? Fewer today, perhaps, than have been to Everest Base Camp. I know more people who have trekked in Nepal than have been out to the back of Craigvinean forest. Once upon a time, before The First World War when manpower was still available to the big estates and before the Forestry Act of 1919, Elrick More was a choice destination for picnics. To ease access to the viewpoint a radial road was dug around the hill allowing an easy pull for a horse and cart or carriage. An example of a restored viewpoint today is Craigvinean's PineCone Point. The modern folly there, with its spectacular view north to Ben Vrackie, is wheelchair accessible because the 'new' path followed a line of the original carriageway as it contours up the hill. Although long obscured and buried by several generations of spruce and pine thickets, the road was recorded in the original Plan for Craigvinean Forest drawn by Thomas Steuart for the Duke of Atholl in 1826. There for the contractor to use as a blueprint.

Elrick More is barely 1,700 ft high. Yet like many a middling hill in Perthshire it stands clear and offers a wide vista. The view from these sub Munros, these less-than-Corbetts is, to my mind, often better than from a high peak putting you more into the surrounding landscape. Another, further along, is Caisteal Dubh. It too is studded with cairns and odd structures, evidence of previous interest of a time when it was visited more often.

What links them both for me is geocaching - the eye-opener, the game changer. This is not the place to explain the sport's mechanics which are simple enough but still, literally, rocket science. Suffice that with a hand-held GPS or a smart phone with the right app you can download co-ordinates from www.geocaching.com and use the network of satellites miles above to navigate in time and space. Geocaching can become your passport to some wonderful out-of-the-way delights, and to jaggy little bits of history across Highland Perthshire, taking you to places you always meant to explore and helping you discover new ones. New to you, that is.

Through geocaching I have picnicked and napped under Perthshire's own Hanging Rock. But a few miles walk from Newton Bridge out of the Sma' Glen. We all survived, no one went missing. Although there was a surreal quality to the afternoon, one of those blazing hot days you can get in early spring after the snow has melted, when all around us dozens of mountain hares still in ermine scampered as if a giant magician had spilled a pocketful of white rabbits. Geocaching has also taken me to Jorum's View of the three lochs (the top of Newtyle Hill, gained across trackless heather); to MacGregor's Cave, a Victorian folly with a fine view of Dunalastair House; to the Queen's Gate, halfway between Dunkeld and Kirkmichael; to the Hidden Waterfall, below Schiehallion; and memorably, to Torr an Eas, once part of the NTS path system around the Linn of Tummel now totally lost to the forest.   Some I had heard of and I had mentally put on the list of places to get around to, long deferred. Others were a complete surprise.

Geocaching isn't just for the lost places. Perthshire, particularly the large area of Highland Perthshire encompassed by Big Tree Country, is a geocaching paradise with 5,000 plus caches within a 25 mile radius of Dunkeld. You could spend hours, days visiting favourite walks, woods and forests again with a completely fresh eye.

The unofficial motto of geocachers is 'Not all who wander are lost'. An in-joke; while we always know where we are, cachers often, very often have difficulty getting to just where we want to be: ground zero. Where the cache is hidden. So we can give the appearance of wandering aimlessly, albeit usually in a five metre radius.

Paul McLennan

To My Little Piebald Pony

My little piebald pony,

you are my dearest friend.

We trot and gallop

through the fields,

on rides I wish would never end.

Whenever I'm riding,

I feel so strong and free,

sitting on your back

is where I long to be.

Isabella Olds
Kinloch Rannoch Primary School

My Visit to Uganda

Jane and Nicky King from our church were the inspiration for my recent trip to Uganda. Approximately fifteen years ago they set up a project to assist in improving the lives of those African people. A group of helpers was organised to visit the village of Kitega (pronounced Chiteega) and, in particular, the school for disabled pupils. After some consideration, I decided that I would apply to join this set of ten volunteers on their worthwhile visit that would last for two weeks. Not as easy as all that though, as preparations and planning were the first steps which included fundraising. One of our group members was an I.T. teacher from Pitlochry High School. He lent his expertise to the trip. It had been decided that it would be beneficial to pupils, aged from six years to late teens, if we were to provide them with Raspberry Computers. Their last computers had been stolen. The necessary medical protection had also to be taken, such as the all-important injections.

Before not too long we were off. I discovered that my main job would be to assist those teachers already working with the children by supporting with English, Reading and Maths, not to mention the more fun activities that took place in the afternoons. I was well prepared for what was to come as I had regularly been studying a daily blog that was compiled by some of our group who were already at the Centre. They were there for two weeks preceding our arrival. I found their blog very informative.

We flew from Glasgow via Amsterdam to an airport near Kampala. After twenty four hours travelling, we arrived at the village by jeep, complete with all our luggage and computer equipment. I was unaware of the countryside during the road journey from the airport as it was night time. Our comfortable beds in the accommodation building, near the school, awaited us. At that stage we were really glad of a good sleep! I adapted to the heat quite well. The accommodation building had been completed just before we arrived and we were proud to be the first people to use it. Our church had done fundraising towards the construction of this block.

Needless to say theirs is a very different culture from ours and we had to get used to their food for a start. This was prepared and cooked for us. It suited me. I liked it. Breakfast was similar to that in Scotland, usually some British style cereal, accompanied by fresh fruit. For other meals you might get foods like rice, potatoes and meat, which could be quite tough, or chicken with gravy. The meat was usually cooked on the bone. In the fields the local people grow sugar cane, coffee, vegetables and fruit such as mangoes, bananas, jack fruit (juicy and sweet), melons and apples.

A typical day's timetable (lessons in English) might be:

BREAKFAST together

Morning School: helping with the Maths. The children had text books to work from and each had a jotter.

BREAK

Spelling with games that helped the pupils to remember the words
Songs (their own songs) and we also taught them new songs

LUNCH

Activities like "Duck, duck, goose" (everybody formed a circle and if you were the goose then you would have to chase the duck round the outside of the circle and hope to catch the person before they could sit down in the spare place in the circle) or "What's the time, Mr Wolf?"

They enjoyed doing a variety of crafts and games like football

TEA for the young people

Later we returned to our accommodation block where we could relax and do our own thing. Here we were glad to have our tea that was cooked for us. In the accommodation block there were a lounge and a kitchen. Two people shared a bedroom. Each bed had its own mosquito net, but even then some people got small bites. We were advised to make sure that we were covered up to avoid bites where possible. However when we played football we usually just wore a strip and a pair of shorts.

There was a modern shower (cold water) and toilet. They had a generator for electricity that was connected just before we left. Three of the many characters stand out in my mind. One child who had malaria and required a special diet, mainly bananas and milk. There was a small amount of money left over from the fundraising so we decided to buy a cow to supply milk for this purpose. We used the remaining money to help create their playground. Daudi (David) who had visited us at the Atholl Centre in Pitlochry I remember fondly, along with another local man who had gone to Dundee to study whom I recognised in Kitega.

We had the privilege of being invited to a wedding during our stay when a male worker got married to a cook from the kitchen. We dressed up in our best clothes for this special occasion. Wearing our smart/casual clothes, as is the custom on such occasions, my group was taken to another village to see businesses that had developed from the Community Bank Scheme. Here a market had been created with a variety of stalls. I remember one man who produced coffee beans and raised pigs to sell to suppliers. We were lucky enough to be driven to the source of the River Nile. I actually saw the water spring where the Nile starts. I was amazed to see huge lizards and some really colourful birds. We went out in a small boat to an island on which there was a signpost which said 'SOURCE OF THE NILE'. Our visit was in October when there can be really heavy bursts of rain accompanied by thunder and lightening. It's about 25 degrees centigrade or more and humid.

I was sad when it was time to return home but I think it made us all realise that we were lucky to have what we have. Through Facebook I can communicate with teachers Brian, who is currently receiving training in teaching children with specific needs, and Millie and Edith. I worked closely with them while I was there. It's possible that I'll go over to Uganda again. I'd like to return!

Chris Meyer

A Moving Tale

The names in this story have been changed to protect the guilty from further embarrassment and teasing, because the following is a true account of one couple's experience of moving house.

After many happy years in an old farmhouse, and with the children grown and in their own homes, Kate and Willie decided to move to a smaller house. Moving day itself was fraught with minor mishaps, as you would expect, but by the end of the day, they were able to go to sleep in their new home. That was the last decent sleep they had for a few weeks.

At breakfast, Willie decided that before handing back the keys, he would go and spring clean the empty house while Kate would stay at the new house unpacking. An exhausted Kate thought this was an excellent idea so happily waved Willie off and then went for a nap.

Back at the old house, Willie entered by the kitchen door. He saw the built-in double oven facing him and thought he would begin by turning on both ovens full blast to let the self - cleaning process start. That done, he went upstairs to clean the bathroom. He turned on all the taps and was wiping surfaces when the smell of smoke filled his nostrils. Remembering too late that the top oven was also the grill and was not self-cleaning, he rushed back to the kitchen to discover flames and smoke belching from the grill. He opened the back door and then grabbed a wet cloth. Now, most people know that to put out a burning grill pan, you lay a damp cloth over it, but not our Willie.

No, Willie decided to use the wet cloth to protect his hands while in his panic, he ran outside with the burning grill pan. Inexplicably, he chose not to put the pan down on the patio, but instead threw it into the field where it landed on the very large, new hay bale the farmer had delivered earlier that morning for his cows to graze upon. The bale caught alight, the cows scarpered, and now Willie was faced with the possibility of burning down not only an entire field, but also the incineration of a prize herd of cows. Thinking fast (!!) he ran to the outside tap, filled a bucket, climbed the fence and doused the bale. He had to repeat this exercise several times before he was satisfied that the fire in the now-saturated bale was out, and that the cows were in no danger.

Trousers ripped on the fencing, shoes splattered with the particular kind of mud only well-fed cows can produce, a relieved Willie made his way back to the house to continue cleaning, annoyed at himself now for having sooty kitchen walls to wash down as well. Leaving his shoes outside, he walked back into the kitchen and through the door opening he saw a large, white, unrecognisable, dusty object on the hall floor. It was at this point he remembered he hadn't turned the bathroom taps off when he went to deal with the fire and yes, the object before him was the hall ceiling, now on the floor! Willie bounded upstairs to find the bath and sink overflowing, the whole of the upstairs landing soaking and a large hole where the middle of the bathroom floor ought to have been.

He calmly turned off the taps, pulled out the plugs, turned the electricity off at the mains, locked the house and went home. He was covered in soot, had torn trousers, soaking feet, stinking shoes and a fully refreshed, if somewhat angry, Kate met him at the door saying: "You'll never guess what happened here while you were gone!"

Willie's reply is not suitable for public consumption but the next time they move house, the cleaning up will be left to the professionals!

Ann Onimus

Over The Years

Over the years, the most frequently asked question has been: 'How is your life in Scotland?' Hungarians, Scottish, friends and family and unknown people on the bus, they all wanted to know how the foreign woman managed in Scotland. 'Well,' I have to tell them, 'I am fine, I am happy here'. I love Scotland and I love my new life. My days go by quietly here in the countryside. Just like many Eastern Europeans, I work hard in the nearby Luxury Golf and Spa Hotel. It does not matter; I do my job and, after that, I enjoy my life. I love to discover Scotland.

I am lucky. Culzean Castle is only 30 minutes by bike and I am a regular visitor there. The ducks recognize me from my orange color jacket and come out of the water! I love the Deer Park and the Walled Garden and I enjoy the view of Arran. This picturesque view is one of my favorites - never the same and always fascinating.

I have so many favorite sights such as Ailsa Craig from Turnberry, Pitlochry Queens View, Glentrool, Urqhart Castle, Stirling, Glencoe....One of my colleagues told me I know Scotland better than some of the Scottish people born here. I know it is not true!

Over the years I've had many visitors from Hungary and all my friends and family members fell in love with Scotland. They, just like me, love the bagpipe music, the friendly people, haggis and Robert Burns. We all love mountains and valleys, the moorland and stone walls.

Sometimes I got homesick and I had to go home to my native land back in Hungary. After many years of savings now I have a lakeside villa in Hungary and I love to be there with my daughters and grandchildren. I enjoy the different weather, the language and I love to tell my grandchildren about Scottish wildlife. They listen excitedly to the stories about the wildlife around my cottage. I have a pheasant family, bunnies and the neighbouring fields full of sheep and cows. They also want to know what the farmer puts into the ground in the springtime and how many lambs are born in the Easter time. We all love the Highland Cows and Belted Galloways that I saw for the first time here.

So, I am really happy here. I am planning to continue to stay to work and live here in the future. When I retire, I imagine myself at home, beside Lake Balaton in Hungary around my friends and family. I also know I'll return to Scotland often, because my half heart is Scottish, but as Hungarian people say:

'An old tree cannot be uprooted'.

Gizella Kecskes

Gizella feeding the ducks at Culzean Castle

Auld Donald's Croft

In the shadow of Ben Vrackie
Midst the heather in the vale
An ancient crofter stood alone
The sign said 'Croft for Sale'
He was too old and feeble
To plough or tend his land
And his only son had run away
Tae join a ceilidh band

Frae the east a Yankee oilman
Arrived upon the scene
He'd seen auld Donald's advert
In a shop in Aiberdeen
He was looking for a wee croft
Tae which he could retire
Tae forget the cares o'business
By muckin' oot the byre

He looked the place all over
Frae back door tae the lobby
And as nature called he wondered
Where a man cuild hae a jobbie
Tae the bottom o'the gairden
Auld Donald showed the way
Tae the wee dry cludgie by the burn
That stands there tae this day

It was just five minutes later
When the Yank he did return
He said: 'There's just one thing that's missing
In your cludgie by the burn
As I was sitting in there
It shocked me to the core
To realise there was no lock
Upon the lavvy door!'

Auld Donald stared in wonder
And shook his grizzled head
Of such athing he'd never heard
And this was what he said:
'Twas Robert Bruce gave us this land
When he stayed here one dreich night
And since thon day no one's ever stole
One bucketful of shite'

Brian Hughes

Nibbles

I have a hamster called Nibbles. He goes on his wheel loads and loads because he loves his wheel. He also likes his pipe to go in. He sleeps in the morning and he's awake in the night, me and my family can't sleep at night because of him. One thing we like about him is when he is asleep. That's the best time ever in the world. He's the best hamster in the world.

In Glen Lyon.........
I see loads of sheep.
I touch the horses in the field.
I smell lavender flowers.
I hear buzzy bees.
I taste juicy blackberries.

Hiba Saleem
Glenlyon Primary School

Atholl Highlanders' Visit to Eglinton

In 1839 the Earl of Eglinton had decided to hold a recreation of a medieval tournament at his castle in Ayrshire; amongst those invited was Lord Glenlyon, later 6th Duke of Atholl, who attended as 'Knight of the Gael' and took a retinue of 56 men from his Estate with 18 pipers and officers. Transporting the men across Scotland was no small undertaking: they assembled in Perth, took a steamer to Dundee and another to Edinburgh. They then travelled by the Edinburgh – Glasgow canal and after a day in Glasgow took a steamer to Ardrossan and walked to Eglinton Castle arriving on August 27th. Over the next few days Lord Glenlyon tilted against other knights, joined in hand to hand combat in a melee and attended a ball on 30 August, the costume from which is still preserved at Blair Castle.

On the return journey the men took the steamer back to Glasgow and the canal boat but they disembarked at Falkirk and marched to Blair Drummond 17 miles away, the home of Lord Glenlyon's fiancé. The following day they marched to Crieff -23 miles - and the next day they reached Dunkeld after 28 miles at 10 pm!

When Queen Victoria visited Dunkeld on her first trip to Scotland in 1842 the number of Highlanders was doubled and they were joined by other local lairds and their men. The cathedral bells were rung, the Royal Standard flown from the tower and a royal salute fired from Stanley Hill. The Queen had lunch in a marquee and was entertained with piping and dancing. In 1844 she stayed at Blair Castle for three weeks and was so impressed with the guard the Highlanders provided that she granted them the Queen's colours, presented in 1845, and thus the right to bear arms.

The Highlanders continued to provide a guard for the Duke and eminent guests throughout the 19th century. They fell into abeyance with the First World War, though pipers did appear for visitors such as the Crown Prince of Japan and King Feisal of Iraq.

The annual parades were revived by the late, 10th Duke of Atholl in 1966, and continue under the present 12th Duke, whose sons are members of the Highlanders.

Queen Victoria's Visit to Dunkeld in 1842

Queen Victoria visited Dunkeld in 1842. This was her first visit to Scotland and Lord Glenlyon, later 6th Duke of Atholl, entertained her to lunch *en route* from Scone to Taymouth Castle. He brought 150 of his own men and invited neighbouring landowners to come with their men, a gathering of 870 in total. A marquee over 100 feet was hired and cooks employed to provide luncheon. On September 7 the Queen received a rousing welcome as her carriage passed through a triumphal arch of heather and juniper at the bridge – she was preceded by pipers, the cathedral bells were rung and a royal salute was fired!

After luncheon a sword dance and reels were performed to pipe music for her entertainment before she left for Taymouth. She must have been impressed as two years later she invited herself for a three week stay at Blair Castle. She so appreciated the Atholl Highlanders guarding her on these visits that in 1845 she granted them the Queen's colour and thus the right to bear arms (carry weapons), a unique privilege they retain to this day. They now consist of about 100 men, including the pipes and drums, all of whom are invited to join by the Duke of Atholl. The present 12th Duke succeeded on the death of his father in May 2012.

Jane Anderson

Atholl Highlander standing in the main hall at Blair Atholl Castle

Loch Ordie

As we follow the fast flowing burns,
We spot rare animals,
Buzzards, Peregrine Falcons and Black Grouse
My ears are filled with their choruses.

Turning the corner, the adrenaline shoots through my body,
The tranquil loch comes into view,
Ice age carved hills break in two,
I see the glistening clear water of Loch Ordie.

I change my gears as I begin to climb the last hill,
Leaning my bike on the deserted fishing huts,
I notice nobody else is here,
Now I can explore.

Carefully I step on the cracked stone steps,
Which bring me right to the loch-side, I cup my hands and let the
Baltic water find them,
I take a refreshing gulp,
It's sweet and delicious!

Skimming the historic stones into the loch,
Paddling in the shallow waters,
Looking out for the Ordie Monster,
And rowing out to the middle of the deep loch
In my wee sailing dinghy.

As I approach the middle of the loch,
There's a disturbance in the water,
As slowly as a snail something is rising out of the bottomless loch,
IT'S THE ORDIE MONSTER!

Charlotte Leishman
Royal School of Dunkeld

Jack's Story

After living in the village of Kinloch Rannoch, which is 20 miles from Pitlochry, for nearly 30 years, I have just moved to Perth. Well, you see, the family had all moved away and there is not much left there for me, so my daughter suggested I would be better off going to Perth. This prompted me to put my name down for a house in Perth. It's more convenient for my daughter to keep an eye on me, as she stays in Comrie, plus you can't be more central for travelling than Perth.

So I have got a lovely flat with the Caledonian Housing Association, just about 20 minutes walk from the centre of Perth, just up from the River Tay. The only disadvantage is that it's located up a hill; however I do have my bus pass. What I like about where I live is that the people are very friendly and it is in a lovely spot. If I want to go anywhere I just go down to the bus station in Perth to catch a bus to Glasgow or Dundee or anywhere in Scotland. You also have the benefit of the library, the theatre and a bit more, so I can't complain. Another huge advantage is accessing my classes. I'm a member of the U3A (University of the Third Age) so previously from the village, it was always tricky to travel to the classes held in Perth. I had to catch the early bus just after 7 am to Pitlochry and then another bus from there to Perth. Occasionally I was lucky enough to get a lift from a friend. So, in that respect, that's another good reason for living in Perth.

Other activities I've tried since I've been here are going to the theatre and the cinema. Recently I attended a debate at Perth Concert Hall. I have always enjoyed attending talks and discussions because I like to hear other people's opinions. Sometimes I agree with them, other times I don't. Even although there were talks and classes on offer around Kinloch Rannoch, the difference between the two places is like night and day. However, one outstanding lecture that I'll always remember in Kinloch

Rannoch was given by a reporter who now lives in the area. He described the situation in Chile when Pinochet took over. He recalled a time when people were herded into a football stadium. He said, 'I was lucky to get out of there alive, because a good number of those present were shot.' There had been a coup with support from the U.S. It was interesting to have the opportunity to hear this information from someone who had actually witnessed the *coup d'etat* first hand. So often reports of such events can be distorted by the media, particularly in the press. This talk left a strong impression on me.

Attempts were made to provide interesting activities in my village. In spite of us trying to set up a Film Club, not many people turned up. In contrast, Perth, to me, is like an oasis, another world with clubs, classes and debates readily available when I investigate. I'm currently attending classes on such subjects as Russia in 1913 and the History of China. I've just completed my Discovery Award and as a direct result of this have become involved in Voluntary Work helping at the complex where I live.

I would say that I've never had such a busy life for a long time. I'm looking forward to visiting my family in Australia next month, especially to see my two grandsons again.   I'll travel to Perth, Australia then on to Brisbane. So I'll be relaxing over there, delighted to see them all again.

Jack Brannan

Jack receiving his Discovery Award from Liz Grant, the Provost of Perth and Kinross

Lee's Enlightenment

Night Mysteries

Fantasy, fairies,
They all come to life
Here in this magical, mystical land.
The eerie moonlight dancers with their lengthy shadows,
Skip and slide through those grand old oaks that stand so tall.
Brown and bare now.
Their leaves departed to create a coloured spectacle,
On the grounds they have sheltered,
As many of those past moons have drifted by.
The place is so tranquil and still.
Walking through the forest till the silence is broken
By the snapping twigs beneath my feet.
Rustlings.
The darkness brings playtime for our nocturnal friends
As they emerge midst the forest floor.

In the distance, the river's in full spate,
Its sound is amplified with every step closer I take.
Its excited water is cascading over the rocks
Like a herd of white horses galloping in a torrent of rage.

Sunny Hours

Pretty pinks too bright
Invigorating yellows.
The magical aura of these magnificent grounds encompass you
Envelop your heart with the courage to engage.
The feeling of warmth filters through your mind.
No negative thoughts will cross the gateway.
Cast your eyes anywhere,
At the end or in between,
The result's the same when you're given the freedom to dream.

Leesa Scott

My Picture

I lived in a small town called Pitlochry for 6 months. This allowed me to change my personality, my character all the way up to changing my profession from chemical engineer to hotelkeeper.My intention of going to Pitlochry was a decision of the school where I was studying English. Thanks to this destination, I could improve the language and I could adapt myself and coexist with people of other nationalities. I had the opportunity to be employed at Pitlochry Hydro Hotel where I gained a great experience and very good relations with my chiefs and co-workers.

During my stay I had the opportunity to attend a free English course in the Pitlochry learning centre, where I met my tutor, Pam McDonald, an extraordinary person of patience and charisma in the class she ran.

Also I had the chance to walk and discover every corner of the town, including knowing the whisky distilleries at Edradour and Blair Atholl. In addition, by being well located geographically, I could take the train to visit other cities accessible from Pitlochry. Unfortunately I could not attend too many festivals and events during the summer, because I had to return to my country Venezuela. I felt very nostalgic for this wonderful place, where the people were kind and nice to me.

I will never forget the great moments and memories which I shared with my colleagues and friends; having a few beers in bars, eating haggis and fish and chips with vinegar, to greeting people regardless of nationality and culture. I hope to return at some point in my life to reconnect with this quiet village and my great friends.

Jorge Fung

A Visit to York

Last month I took a few days off from work. I decided to make a visit to the city of York. During my three day trip, I realized that all I had heard about the city's beauty is true. York is a walled city, situated at the confluence of the Rivers Ouse and Foss in North Yorkshire, England. The city has a rich heritage and offers a wealth of historic attractions. It's one of the most visited cities in England.

Just outside the train station I could see a beautiful view. It was sunny and the medieval walls of York were in front of me. This wall is one of the hallmarks of the city. You can walk on the wall, as it surrounds the city, and see stunning views at the same time.

After checking in and leaving my luggage in the hotel, I started to explore and discover this wonderful city. I dedicated the first afternoon to walking around the city and getting lost in its streets. When you walk along these streets, it looks as if you have gone back in time. They are narrow streets, lined with shops and traditional English pubs.

The next day I visited Clifford's Tower and the cathedral. Clifford's Tower is the only remnant of York Castle. It is located on an artificial manmade mound and there is practically nothing inside, just a room, but you can figure out how it was before. In this place you can go up and see wonderful views too.

After visiting Clifford's Tower, I kept walking through the streets towards the cathedral. I think The Minster is the most impressive place in the city. It's a wonder, both outside and inside. Its impressive figure dominates the city landscape. You can't describe it in words, you have to go and see it. When you are inside you realize that you could spend hours and hours examining the wonderful stained glasses. Some parts of the cathedral were being restored and because of that I couldn't see the largest stained glass window. It is said that it is the same size as a tennis court. In spite of that, it's worth visiting and I strongly recommend people to go.

After visiting the cathedral, I came back to the city centre because I wanted to go to a very famous street in York. After a few turns, the centre can be a bit rambling. I ended up in this famous street. It is a rather narrow street, but very quaint and pretty. It is said that it's a street which has barely changed since 1400. It was the street where the number of butchers, at one time, was 25, hence its name, "The Shambles" – from an old Anglo Saxon word "fleshammels" meaning shelves of meat.

There are shops where you can see the same spikes where they would have hung the meat. There are shops of all kinds and in this street you can stop off at one of the oldest tea shops in the city.

Every time I went into the centre from my hotel, I had to cross a bridge over the River Ouse. From there you can watch the boats they use for trips along the river. So, as I was curious, I decided that the next morning I would go for a boat trip. I must say I didn't choose the best day for it, it was very cold!!! The trip takes 45 minutes and you can learn about the history of the city, so it was a worthwhile experience, despite the cold.

After the boat trip, I went for a visit to the ruins of St. Mary's Abbey. There isn't very much remaining, just some walls and a sarcophagus, but we can figure out how big and important that abbey was. It is very close to the river and surrounded by gardens so it's a good place to go for a walk and relax.

The next day, I had to return to Pitlochry, so I dedicated myself to walking and exploring and seeing still more of this city of York. For me it is one of the most beautiful cities I have ever seen. I would certainly recommend everyone to go and visit it.

Lourdes Hurtado Gonzalez

A Wartime Country Boyhood

I was born in 1932 in the village of Caputh, twelve miles north of Perth. Conditions were pretty primitive, lighting was paraffin lamps and heating from coal fires. The village was owned by the Lyles of Glendelvine (of Tate and Lyle the sugar firm).

The first memory I can recall was when I was three. I was taken to my paternal grandfather's smallholding, *Blinkbonny* (about half a mile away), to get a white male albino rabbit with red eyes from my uncle Ken. His home was a hutch my father made. I called the rabbit 'Jock'. Jock was fifteen when he died.

Education

My next memory is of starting school at Glendelvine which children from Caputh and Spittalfield and the surrounding area attended. No nursery to break you in; at age five you were right in at the deep end! I was lucky. The infant teacher was Miss Lumsden, a lovely lady of about twenty five years old. She never married and was ninety six when she died. At the age of eight I moved into the middle room. The teacher was Miss Menzies. Talk about chalk and cheese! The belt was never out of her hand. Three years with her then into the Headmaster's room. His name was Mr Taylor. He was Captain of the Auxiliary Force which consisted of men too old for the services and men in reserved occupations like agriculture. The year was 1943. I was eleven and we were still at war with Germany. Mr Taylor's son was a captain in the Black Watch. Every day after playtime my cousin, Willie Roy, was sent to Caputh Post Office on his bike (half a mile) to get the *'Dundee Courier'*.

At primary school homework was given every day. I had to read a page of "Little Red Hen" every night. I rattled it off, but Miss Lumsden was suspicious. She took me out and told me to recite it again. She turned to page two and I recited page one again – I had learned it off by heart. I got a note home to see I didn't do that again. We had enough time to play between school and jobs we did. Games included hide and seek, kick-the-can, skipping, fun with old tennis balls and conkers in the autumn. Everything had its season and the time just came around. At eleven years old I was Dux of the school. I stayed on for a year after passing the eleven plus exam to sit an exam for the McDougall Bursary. Without the money from that I could not go on to the secondary school. The money paid for your travel and your school books. No free education then in 1946.

Mr Taylor was promoted to a post at Invergowrie. His replacement was Mr Cameron, a horrible little man. He had been deputy head of Craigie (Western District School in Perth). He only took the Glendelvine job in the hope of getting the head's job back in Craigie when the then head retired (he did eventually get it) His interest in Glendelvine was nil.

I did three years' secondary education at Balhousie Boys School which was situated in Dunkeld Road in Perth. There I studied English, History, Geography and Maths, Technical Subjects, woodwork, mechanics and technical drawing along with science. Physics and Chemistry were taught in the old Perth Academy in Rose Terrace next to the North Inch. To get there we had to go down Low Street, cross Balhousie Street and carry on down Barrosa Place.

Work as a Boy

When I was seven I started to work lifting tatties at Mr Moan's Middleton Farm. A drill was divided into bits, one bit per lifter. The field had become bigger so Mr Moan asked mothers if their eldest children could manage a half bit. Accordingly Nancy Beekie, Elspeth Campbell, my cousin Willie Roy and I got a half bit each. The next summer when I was eight I was picking raspberries on Mr Jeffries' farm. The rate was a farthing a pound. A farthing was a quarter of an old penny (or 960 in a pound!) I also cleaned and creosoted henhouses for him. I later did other farm work until I left school. On Sunday from the age of eleven to fifteen I was organ boy at Caputh Church. The salary was £2 and 10 shillings per year (or £2.50 in 'new' money). This was paid once a year, on 28 November, so less than a shilling a week.

The War

There was a large map on the wall at school and we were kept up to date with the war. I wrote about the Home Guard. If you ever saw Dad's Army on television that's what they were like! We had dug trenches in waste ground at the side of Caputh Brae when we went up to play soldiers. One Sunday afternoon the Home Guard took them over because they had an exercise. Dave Low, Glendelvine Estates forester, was going to lie down in the flower bed in front of our house. My mum shouted out to him: 'Dave, how are you not going to flatten my chrysanthemums?' 'Good God, woman,' he said, 'don't you know there is a war on?!' She answered: 'I should think so with my man in Africa!' From 1939 until the end of the war we had to carry our gas masks everywhere. In 1940 we had an influx of evacuees from Glasgow and some mothers came with their children. When they found out that the nearest pub and chip shop were five miles away they went back home; they would rather face the bombs. What they left were wet beds and an infestation of head lice. Food, of course, was rationed and coupons were needed for food and clothes, but we managed.

Our local war excitement was when a pilot, on his maiden flight from Scone aerodrome, crashed his yellow Tiger Moth biplane into power lines south of Caputh Bridge, landing in the Tay. A Miss Ballantine took a fishing boat out to rescue him. It took eight horses to pull the wreckage from the river. When the lines were put back up they were painted yellow as a warning to airmen. Another time a German plane, fleeing from a raid on Clydebank dropped two bombs in Perthshire. One landed in a bog near

Bankfoot and the other made a hole in a berry field near Blairgowrie.

The Canadian Royal Forestry Corps spent two years cutting big timber on the Murthly Estate. They built their own log cabins. The east drive to Murthly Castle had an avenue of huge silver firs whose lower branches touched the ground. The army put two nissen huts under each one and stored ammunition there.

My father was called up in 1940 and was posted to the Royal Aircraft Anti-artillery regiment spending time on Clydeside and Middleborough before being posted to Africa. He was in Nairobi then Egypt where he was wounded. He was only home for two weeks when he was taken to Stracathro Hospital where he was diagnosed with TB and he remained there until 1956 when he died at only 48. He went to the army when I was eight and my siblings younger, so you could say we never really knew him. Apart from him being away and the incidents recorded the only effect the war had on our community was the loss of three lives; Jim O'Brien went down with the *Dorsetshire,* Dave Baird was killed in Damascus and Harry Paul was killed in the Middle East on the last day of the war.

These were the days of make-do-and-mend. Recycling isn't a new idea! These are my memories from infancy until I was fifteen and I hope they will be of interest!

Bob Dingwall

Four Near Misses

*In the last book 'Life as We Know It', Allan Thomson wrote of his
experiences of ditching in his Barracuda aircraft off Orkney in the
Second World War. He was part of the squadron of 21 Barracudas
that successfully disabled the much-feared German battleship 'Tirpitz'
in April of 1944 when it was berthed deep inside a Norwegian fjord in
the far north of that country. Here he describes some near misses
which were an occupational hazard at a time of terrible and deadly
conflict.*

I served as a telegraphist air gunner (TAG) with 827 and 830
Squadrons which were made up of specialist Barracuda bombers.
The steep dive angle of the bombers was severe, officially 87
degrees. Within a month of the squadron's formation in May of
1943 we were posted to Hatston in Orkney. On the way north I
had been scheduled to fly in one of the aircraft but at the last
minute there was a crew change – I went up by train and ferry –
and the aircraft I was due to be in dived and crashed into the
ground on a landing approach to Arbroath. The TAG killed was P/O
Wiggins from Yorkshire. Fumes from a leak in the hydraulic system
had anaesthetised the pilot who slumped forward causing the
aircraft to plunge dive. This was my first near miss. A replacement
aircraft was flown north after a couple of weeks. On landing one
undercart wheel failed to lower and when the pilot landed on the
grass he had to hold the plane level until his speed dropped
enough to attempt to stop. Even at that the port wing touched the
ground and the aircraft spun quickly round but there was little
damage.

Another scare was when we were on a practice bombing exercise
on a supply carrier ship. The mock mission was called "Find, Fix
and Strike". Our aircraft spotted the target and had to shadow it
while the other eleven aircraft, which had returned to base to
refuel, joined us. After the mock attack we flew back but had less
than 10 gallons of fuel left in the tank. We had been airborne for

nearly four and a half hours and had pushed the flight time to fuel ratio to the limit! Pressure was constant. Literal pressure on the ears was a real problem with such steep, fast dive-bombing. I knew a pilot who thought he wouldn't be able to pull his aircraft out of a dive and his jet back hair developed white patches overnight. When my own aircraft went into its dive on our *Tirpitz* mission the negative G effect was so violent that a notepad elasticated to my knee flew up level with my face and my head hit the canopy.

The second near miss happened in an area of the Clyde when we were on exercises. We were to land on the carrier *HMS Furious* but when the Barracuda touched down on the deck we were not stopped by the four arrestor wires. The belief was that if an aircraft was not stopped by the arrestor wires it would be unable to regain sufficient speed to take off again and would crash into the sea. Our tail hook (which was needed to catch the wires) had jumped back up and jammed. Luckily the pilot was able to get just enough speed to get us airborne again and, despite circling the vessel several times was unable to get the hook down again. We flew instead to Macrihanish where we were able to land safely. Another crew weren't so lucky. While we were below one day having lunch we heard a very loud thump on the deck above, followed by a terrific splash. When we looked out of a porthole we saw crew scrambling out of a rapidly-sinking Barracuda which had gone over the side. They were rescued.

A third near miss occurred again by the intervention of fate. We were due to fly north to the Shetland Skerries from Orkney to drop practice bombs on pre-set targets. 18 planes were due to fly in pairs, with around a 200-yard clearance between the two columns. As our aircraft taxied along the runway smoke and sparks were coming from the tail. We pulled onto the grass and jumped out to discover the tail wheel tyre had blown and the metal was worn halfway to the hub. Meanwhile the plane alongside which our Barracuda was due to fly blew up in mid-air;

had we been in the formation as planned it's likely the explosion would have taken us with it.

It was ironic that near misses didn't happen in active combat situations. The fourth was when our squadron was practising what was known as fighter evasion in formation, effectively the planes flying in a corkscrew-type manoeuvre to mitigate against stern attacks. The usual TAG crewman for a particular aircraft was for some reason unable to fly and two different senior staff had asked a chap called Andy Anderson and I to replace him, neither aware the other had done so. By the time I had collected my kit and got to the aircraft, Andy was already sitting in it. He said: "as I'm already here I might as well stay in". Little did he know what he was saying! Once airborne and at the first pass of the Seafire fighter making the dummy attack, the fighter's pilot watched in horror as the two aircraft went into the corkscrew manoeuvre in opposite directions, which caused them to come together causing a huge, sickening crash. A search around the Ailsa Craig area proved fruitless. Not a trace of any of the six air crew was found.

Flight crew were not the only victims – I saw a ground crewman's head split open by a flying wheel chock, and another nearly frozen to death when an aircraft took off with him still working on the tail-end fuselage.

Allan Thomson

So many combatants lost their lives in that awful conflict. It's almost surreal in a time of relative peace to read Allan's matter-of-fact story and understand the constant exposure to risk and death that brave men like Allan faced every day.

Pitlochry War memorial

Of all those many Summer visitors who sit in this
bright public garden very few think of those who
went bravely out into Death's dark night,
those whose names are remembered here, black-embossed
clear against granite's silvery gloss,
names that perpetually commemorate this district's grievous loss...
Those who gave up their right to fun,
who lost their rightful place in the sun.

Younger generations sit and careless gulp 'Coke',
engrossed with noisy laughter and thoughtless jokes
they know nothing of that generation who gave all,
who forfeited Life's brightest joys, its noblest hopes.
Is it only us old enough to remember the last World War
who can truly feel for that lost generation who died
in the Black Obscenity of the First World War?...
only us who are so deeply moved by those endless rows
of white war graves that flow wave upon ceaseless wave?

We think of those young shepherds who left their
quiet Perthshire hills – places soon to be bereft of most
human life – who left their weeping bairns and their soon
to be widowed distraught young wives.
So many went from those Highland homes never to return,
hardy men who would never more rejoice in ripening Summer sun,
never more share in another harvest won.
They exchanged their demanding Highland soil –
that soil they inarticulately loved –
for the pitiless madness of filthy Flanders mud.
As, proudly waved and cheered, those brave young Perthshire men
entrained in Pitlochry's small railway station none knew
how terribly few would win through to see this hometown again.
These young Territorial Army soldiers proud wear their
Black watch kilts and naively think themselves bound for

exciting adventures; almost none have been out of this country,
many have never ventured out of their own county.
Together those great comrades willingly faced many hazards,
together they endured dreary months in Flanders sodden
trenches,
then they went "over the top" together and died together,
mere cannon-fodder...
So many bright young lives so culpably ended!

From comfortably remote headquarters had issued decisions
that translated into a deadly spate –
a ceaseless flood of spilling British blood.
So many young soldiers ruthlessly mown down by machine-guns
which kill with efficient mechanical skill...
methodical maniac killings with unfeeling
slaughterhouse precision.

Those many British dead are victims of a hidebound
British General's entrenched mind,
a cavalry officer who thought of wars fought
with sword and lance, an officer blind to all reason,
to all compassion, as he orders yet more futile,
blindly suicidal attacks.
His victims are slaughtered by storms of bullets,
vicious bullets that with savage glee turn humans
into grotesquely torn puppets...
puppets whose legs unavailing kick,
whose hands vainly claw, whose blood dripping arms
spasmodic jerk as they dangle atrociuosly brambled
on barb-wire's savage spikes.

Fortunate are those with bright arterial blood pouring...
they quickly died;
tragic are those with lesser wounds who,
hanging entangled in barbed wire's ruthless grip
take so terribly long to die...

how awful is all their urgent imploring,
how vicious is all their foul swearing,
but all those prayers to a seeming uncaring God
and all that Devilish cursing and swearing
are all equally unavailing.

Many other of our tragic wounded drown in the watery Hell
of rain-filled shell holes, while yet more fall and flounder
in that foul quagmire of artillery-churned mud...
there, gasping and weeping, they end up fathoms deep
in that inescapable insatiable Flanders mud,
that alien sea of mud that greedily gulped
an entire generation's blood.

Truly it would be a desperate shame if all those named
on Pitlochry's War Memorial – all those who fought and died –
should be completely forgot,
should never be paid the tribute
of an occasional sad sighing silent thought.

Robert O. Scott

John Fielder 97

Some of the contributors to BreadAtholl Brose are;

Kenneth Steven

End of the Year

Agnes (Agi) Forgacs

My Stone

Charlotte Leishman

Loch Ordie

Gladys Meek

Gladys' Story

John Henley

The Musings of Haggis John

Gizella Kecskes

Over The Years

Rita Murray

Dunkeld and Birnam Reminisences

Josh Cameron

Priceless

Chris Meyer

My Visit to Uganda

Jack Brannan

Jack's Story

Hiba Saleem

Nibbles

Lin Frearson

A Sense of Place

Anne Walker

Letter from Brazil

Fred Smith

My Grannys' Heilan' Hame

Pat Edward

Pat's Story

Bec Cameron

After the Rain

Joe Baker

Off Road Biking

Robert O. Scott

Pitlochry War Memorial

David Caldwell

A Huge Adventure

Ann I McIntyre

Glen Tilt

Nicola Hannen

Highland Perthshire

Isabella Olds

To My Little Piebald Pony

Paul McLellan

Lost Places

Skye Murray-Trail

Dear Diary

Wilma Leighton

Onward and Upward

Jacqueline Smith

Perils of Country Living

Iain Walker

Bomb in the Bog - two stories in one

144

*Drawing by Hannah Watt
Kinloch Rannoch Primary*

Lightning Source UK Ltd.
Milton Keynes UK
UKOW07f0624010515

250730UK00007B/31/P

BreadAtholl Brose

a

compilation of writing

from

Highland Perthshire

Front Cover - Early winter day at Rotmell Loch, photo taken by Janet Hunt

Artwork by Leo Claughton, Kinloch Rannoch Primary School